Foreword

It is self-evident that the imperatives of sustainability will increasingly be an explicit part of the background to many of the major policy decisions that await us in the 21st century. In order to highlight this, and to examine the role that science and technology can play in guiding policies aimed at promoting sustainability, the world's national academies of science, under the leadership of the InterAcademy Panel, are meeting in Tokyo in May 2000. I do not expect their conclusions to make comfortable reading.

One of the least comfortable themes is sustainable consumption. Taken seriously, it is likely to require major changes in the lifestyles of the most developed countries—something that none of us will find easy.

These are difficult issues, conceptually let alone socially and politically. But natural and social science have important contributions to make, by analysing some of the basic ideas and assumptions, by providing quantitative data to inform rigorous thinking and by offering new options. The sciences cannot by themselves solve the problems, but they can provide guidelines to the policy-makers.

As one contribution to the Tokyo discussions, national academies of Europe have combined to produce this volume of papers. They cover a wide range of issues: energy, biodiversity, land use, water, wood, fisheries, agriculture, economics and trade, legal and social issues, and the possibilities of curbing consumption in affluent societies. All the papers make valuable contributions to our understanding of the underlying problem, and I hope they will be studied closely by a wide readership.

I should like to express my warmest thanks to Professor Brian Heap, Foreign Secretary and Vice-President of the Royal Society, and to his colleagues for their work in bringing this book to fruition. I hope it will stimulate a constructive approach to matters that affect us all.

Sir Aaron Klug, OM, PRS
President, The Royal Society

March 2000

THE ROYAL
SOCIETY

Towards sustainable consumption
A European perspective

TO BE
DISPOSED
BY
AUTHORITY

Edited by Brian Heap and Jennifer Kent

The Royal Society, 6 Carlton House Terrace, London SW1Y 5AG, UK
and
35 Dorchester Close, Old Road, Headington, Oxford OX3 8SS, UK

Published May 2000
ISBN 0 85403 537 0

The Royal Society, 6 Carlton House Terrace, London SW1Y 5AG.
Tel: +44 020 7839 5561 Fax: +44 020 7930 2170
www.royalsoc.ac.uk

Registered Charity (No. 207043)

Contents

Introduction

by Brian Heap, ForSecRS

The Royal Society, 6 Carlton House Terrace, London SW1Y 5AG, UK

Such is the availability of food, energy and manufactured goods in many Western countries that for the first time in history we are faced with a multitude of consumer products and a deficiency of mechanisms to defend against excessive consumption. Physiological mechanisms have evolved to defend against body weight loss but only weak mechanisms exist to defend against excessive body weight gain when food is abundant. The current epidemic of obesity is caused largely by an environment that promotes high intake through excessive consumption. Relatively inexpensive, highly palatable, energy-rich foods are available coupled with a lifestyle that discourages other forms of energy expenditure such as physical activity and promotes unsustainable forms of transportation. The result is that the number of people who are over-nourished and overweight rivals the number who are undernourished and underweight.

Unsurprisingly, the concept of sustainable consumption is not popular with governments. It wins few votes and provides an implied threat to competitiveness, employment and profitability. Instead, citizens are encouraged to spend, spend and spend. Yet consumption is at the centre of sustainable development (which everyone seems to want) and one of the great challenges of the next century must be to make the concept intelligible by a better understanding of the patterns of consumption, what drives them, and how the efficiency of consumption can be improved (see Appendix A).

Population growth would seem at first sight to be the cause of unsustainable consumption. The world's population is now 6 billion people and the figure continues to grow by 214,000 each day or nearly 80 million people each year. Although the growth rate itself has actually declined from about 2% in 1970 to less than 1.4% in 2000, if the population continues to grow at the present rate then it will have doubled by the year 2050.

Two examples taken from the joint statement issued by the Royal Society and the US National Academy of Sciences (Appendix B) show that consumption is dictated also by economic activity, technology choices, social values, institutions and policies. The first example concerns the population growth of the UK (now 118,000 per year) which causes more than double the carbon dioxide emissions of the 2.4 million people added to the population in Bangladesh each year. The second concerns the richest 20% of the world's population which has increased very little numerically but has raised its per capita consumption of meat and timber two-fold, its car ownership four-fold and its use of plastics five-fold since 1950. The poorest 20% (which have increased in number appreciably) has raised its consumption hardly at all.

Economists see consumption in terms of the generation of utility, anthropologists and sociologists in terms of social meanings, and scientists in terms of the human transformation of materials and energy so that they become less available for future use, or have a negative impact and threaten human health, welfare or other things people value. Since less developed countries have the right to a standard of living comparable to that of the more developed, the potential severity of the consumption problem is emphasized by future projections concerning China and India. When their standard of living reaches a level approaching that of more developed countries the impact on global consumption patterns and resources will be immense (see Myers in this volume).

The United Nations has completed a series of five conferences on major issues of long-term global significance (Environment at Rio de Janeiro in1992; Population at Cairo in 1993; Poverty at Copenhagen in 1994; Women at Beijing in 1995; Cities at Istanbul in 1996). None of these conferences focused on the crucial issue of sustainable consumption. The informal network of the World's Academies, the InterAcademy Panel on International Issues (IAP), has organized preparatory activities at regional centres throughout the world, including extensive work on sustainable development and consumption. These will culminate in an international conference to be held in Tokyo in May 2000 to address the subject Transition to Sustainability. This volume contains the outcome of one of the regional discussions in Europe between several academies and provides additional background papers which focus on sustainable consumption. Authors were invited to prepare short papers on various aspects of Sustainable Consumption highlighting the main issues for one of the sessions in the Tokyo meeting. The papers will appear on the Web as a sourcebook to encourage a wider debate of this important topic. See

http://www4.nas.edu/oia/iap/IAPHome.nsf/all/2000+Conference

The papers are introduced by a detailed review of the dimensions of the global problem. Authors then show how security of land tenure in Europe has given improvements in land productivity over many centuries and the serious questions that have emerged about the unsustainability of certain agricultural systems. Disturbing evidence is recorded of human consumption and activities which have threatened biodiversity, created a serious wood deficiency in Europe (with its impact on rainforests of the tropics), and contaminated freshwater to such extent that only substantial investment will correct the danger. The potential of science and technology to address these problems should not be underestimated. Indeed, the forebodings of the Reverend Robert Malthus in his celebrated essay over 200 years ago have so far been circumvented because of the spectacular advances in science and technology.

The unpredictability of science is well attested and some would claim that expert scientists are no better than members of the general public in foreseeing the scientific and technological future. Admittedly, the future is notoriously difficult to predict, but, as Nobel Laureate and inventor of holography, Dennis Gabor, wrote, 'futures can be invented'. This constructive approach raises the important question of whether the concept of sustainable consumption will become a priority for the future before it is forced upon us? Little support will be gained unless policy-makers, politicians and consumers (you and I included!) are persuaded that it would lead to an improvement in the quality of life, and that changes in consumer behaviour would make a difference. What is becoming clear is the complexity of the underlying drivers of consumption. Behavioural scientists may successfully plumb the depths from which adult choices are determined, but whether it will be in time to advise on the factors that persuade people to adapt their lifestyles in the face of finite resources will probably be a close call. Nonetheless, there are clues from sociological studies that greater awareness of the importance of environmental quality, social equity and economic development could lead to better judgements about what consumers will and will not do.

Material science, particularly fashionable in recent years, is one discipline that offers hope for the future. Steel consumed per person either remains constant or more usually goes down as the income per person increases, and the principle seems to be true for many engineering materials, although not for commodities that are scarce or cannot be recycled. Kelly (1998; see Náry-Szabó in this volume) says the explanation lies in the 'cleverness, skill and ingenuity of the engineers' concerned with production, fabrication of useful artefacts and their distribution to the consumer. The pessimists say that although new knowledge can assist sustainability, the modern methods of intensive extraction, processing and disposal are unsustainable. If the world's population used materials as intensively as the average American, usage would increase six-fold and environmental damage would also rise.

Sustainable consumption as a concept is a hotbed of controversy, as the above example typifies. Similarly, recommendations about energy consumption and how to improve it, or the carrying capacity of the planet and how to assess it, provide further examples of areas of dispute. Clearly, science and technology alone will not provide a route map towards sustainable consumption—the concept is just too complex. Scientists and technologists will need to work more closely with economists, policy-makers and lawyers if there is to be real progress. Therefore, in the final chapters experts from non-scientific, yet highly relevant fields were invited to help build the bridges between science and society and to stimulate anyone new to the concept of sustainable consumption to become aware of the exciting opportunities and demanding challenges that lie ahead. It is time to bridge the cultures and here is a man-made opportunity!

This volume is published by the Royal Society as a contribution to its Science in Society series in which matters of urgency and global significance are aired in the public arena. We would like to thank all authors who have contributed generously of their time, to the staff of the Royal Society for their expertise which enabled the book to appear on time, and to those members of European academies who helped to plan and realise this venture.

Sustainable consumption: the meta-problem

Norman Myers

Upper Meadow, Old Road, Headington, Oxford OX3 8SZ, UK

Background

The twin problems of environment and population are now being joined by a third, consumption, with all that this implies for the ultimate goal of sustainable development. In many respects, consumption will probably prove to be the least tractable of the three interlinked problems, in that consumption patterns and expectations are deeply entrenched in most societies and cultures. However, change will come, whether by design or by default. Present consumption–or, rather, excessive and wasteful consumption—by affluent communities cannot be sustained for environmental reasons alone, as exemplified by the fossil-fuel–CO_2 connection to global warming. In more general terms, there is much evidence (Ehrlich & Ehrlich 1996; Kates *et al.* 1988; Meadows *et al.* 1992; Millman 1991; Pimentel *et al.* 1999; see also Wackernagel, this volume) that the Earth's carrying capacity is already being exceeded by the present six billion people and their lifestyles. Equally to the point, present consumption in developing nations—meagre as these levels are for the three billion people (out of a 4.8 billion total) who account for only 5% of the global economy—cannot rise to levels desired by many citizens, if only because of the sheer numbers of potential consumers. For an illustrative example see Box 1, on China with its 1.2 billion people. Fortunately there are many opportunities to relieve consumption pressures, whether through shifts in lifestyles or enhanced technologies, both of which can be promoted by a range of policy initiatives.

Essentially, this paper proposes that the often extravagant and wasteful consumption of affluent communities constitutes an environmental constraint that is ever more constraining for rich and poor alike, and demands the application of science, technology and policies to address the problem. Furthermore, the skewed consumption patterns between rich and poor might well mean that the point is being approached when—contrary to much past experience—the poor are poor in part because the rich are rich. Worse, the gap between rich and poor is growing. In 1970 the ratio was 30:1; today it is 74:1 (United Nations Development Programme 1998).

During 1995 the 730 million people of Europe emitted some six billion tonnes of CO_2 to the global atmosphere; this was 26% of worldwide emissions (CO_2 being the gas that generates roughly half of global warming processes). Europe's contribution was double that of China's 1.2 billion people. All nations will be affected by global warming, whether they are major or minor sources of CO_2. Industrialized nations' citizens as a whole generate three-quarters of other wide-ranging pollutants, as well as toxic chemicals and hazardous wastes.

Much the same applies to depletion of the world's non-renewable natural resources. To cite only a single instance—especially significant because it relates to the capacity to provide food—over one-fifth of the world's topsoil has been eroded away and nearly one-third of croplands has been lost to land degradation in just the past 40 years, leading to a net decline in croplands per person (Pimentel *et al.* 1995).

Since the middle of the twentieth century, humankind has consumed more natural resources (and caused more pollution and waste) than in all previous human history. This consumption outburst can be illustrated by a few examples that also demonstrate the roles of the affluent sectors of the global community.

- Since 1950 the global economy has quintupled. Consumption of grain, beef and mutton has tripled, as has that of water, whereas paper consumption has risen sixfold. The burning of fossil fuels has grown nearly fourfold, and carbon emissions likewise (Brown *et al.* 1999).
- Since 1950 the richest one-fifth of humankind has doubled its consumption of energy, meat, timber, steel and copper per person, and quadrupled its car ownership, whereas the poorest one-fifth of humankind has increased its general consumption per person hardly at all. Today the richest one-fifth consumes 45% of all meat and fish, the poorest one-fifth 5%; 58% of all energy, compared with 4%; and 84% of all paper, compared with 1.1%. The richest one-fifth owns 87% of the world's vehicles, compared with 1% owned by the poorest one-fifth (United Nations Development Programme 1998).
- With less than 5% of the world's population, the USA uses nearly 30% of the Earth's resources. Yet the 'American dream' and the lifestyles of other affluent nations, notably those of Europe, are becoming a model for new consumers in China, India, Brazil, Mexico, Turkey and Russia, among several other leading nations. Indeed, these new consumers already total 800 million, or as many as the long-established consumers in rich nations (Myers & Kent 2000).

There is nothing intrinsically wrong with affluent communities' consuming a large percentage of natural resources if those resources remain plentiful and can be recycled. For iron and steel, 85% is consumed by the top 20% of people, 55% being recycled—and the top 20% do not thereby limit the consumption of poor people. Indeed, the affluent communities' conversion of natural resources into human capital often enhances human welfare all round. It is of scant consequence that the average American consumes 115 times as much paper as the average Indian, provided that the American recycles most of the paper (at present only 41% is recycled). Much more significant is that the average American consumes 227 times as much gasoline as the average Indian (United Nations Development Programme 1998). The key question is whether consumption uses resources or uses them up.

The current decline of the natural-resource base might well prove to be minor compared with what will probably ensue in the light of exploitation pressures ahead. Cropland is projected to fall from today's meagre 0.27 ha per person to only half as much within 30 years (Engelman & LeRoy 1995). Already over half of the available freshwater runoff is used, an amount that could rise to three-quarters by 2025 through projected population growth alone, i.e. without allowing for any increase in consumption per person. Worse, the number of water-short people today, 500 million, could well soar to three billion by the year 2025—an outcome that would be especially critical for the prospects of feeding humanity in view of agriculture's dependence on water (Postel *et al.* 1996). Humans are co-opting *ca.* 40% of plants' net annual growth on land, leaving 60% for the millions of other species. What will happen when human numbers double and people demand more products from plants?

Of course these global constraints apply in differentiated fashion at regional levels. Water supplies in Europe are generally plentiful, although supplies for agriculture are sometimes limited in parts of Spain and Greece, for example.

Energy

Consider a proxy indicator of consumption's impact: energy use per person, which has a primary role in virtually all human activities that are environmentally adverse. Developed nations consume 70% of all commercial energy, although developing nations' share is expected to rise to 40% by 2010. Some 85% of commercial energy comes from fossil fuels and 7% from nuclear power (World Resources Institute 1998). Despite its many benefits, commercial energy has great capacity to harm the environment through pollution impacts, manifested through urban smog, acid rain and global warming, for example, and through radioactive wastes from nuclear fuels.

The energy problem is epitomized by cars. In 1950 there were 2.5 billion people and 50 million cars. Today, with rather more than twice as many people, there are ten times as many cars (over 70% of them in the USA and Europe). Within another 25 years and with 40% more people, the total number of motor vehicles worldwide might well top one billion. Motor vehicles account for over 15% of all CO_2 emissions (25% in the UK) (Royal Commission on Environmental Pollution 1994). Nations in the Organization for Economic Co-operation and Development (OECD) have 16% of the world's population but emit two-thirds of all CO_2 emissions from motor vehicles worldwide. Global energy use for transportation is predicted to rise by at least 50% during the period 1993—2010, and by twice as much in developing countries (World Resources Institute 1998). In 1995 as many new cars were sold in Asia as in western Europe and North America combined. Were the world to match Americans' present car ownership by 2025, the global total would be 13 times greater than today's.

Grain

Next, consider grain, which is significant in that there is no more important activity for humans than feeding themselves, and grain accounts for 75% of food calories worldwide. With 20% of the world's population, the developed nations consume almost 50% of the world's grain; this disproportionate consumption contributes to reduced consumption on the part of developing nations. Many of the three billion people in nations with a gross national product per person of less than $700 have to spend more than half of their cash incomes on food, which means that even a marginal increase in food prices can tip them over the edge into malnutrition if not starvation.

Nor can there be much relief ahead, given recent agricultural trends. Since 1981 there has been a 6.6% shrinkage in the world's grainlands, and since 1990 there has been only marginal growth in irrigation water supplies (critical because irrigated lands, comprising 17% of all croplands, produce 35% of our food). Grain shortages are likely to continue to mount, even though global population growth of 78 million people a year requires a parallel growth in grain production of 25 million tonnes, and more still to reflect enhanced nutrition and rising affluence.

As people become more affluent, they consume more grain indirectly. Some 34% of the world's grain is fed to livestock each year (over 50% in Europe, 67% in the USA). Americans consume 800 kg of grain per year, whereas Italians consume only half as much, and live longer. If the 1998 grain harvest of almost 1.9 billion tonnes were evenly distributed worldwide, it would support 2.5 billion people at the American level of consumption, five billion at the Italian level, or ten billion at the Indian level of 200 kg per year. If Americans were to cut their grain intake by a mere 16%, this would save 35 million tonnes of grain a year (Brown *et al.* 1999)—enough in principle to make up the diets of 870 million people, or more than the number chronically malnourished today.

The future prospect could be even more difficult. If recent production and consumption trends persist until 2030, then even China alone, with its fast-rising affluence, could be seeking 100–200 million tonnes of grain from overseas (as compared with a 1995 total of 200 million tonnes for more than 100 grain-importing countries). This will drive up grain prices to unprecedented levels for those developing nations looking for another 190 million tonnes of grain (Brown 1995).

Consumption in Europe: problems and opportunities

Now let us look at an illustrative list of ways in which unsustainable consumption is occurring in Europe, followed by ways in which Europe is already taking measures to make the transition towards sustainable consumption.

Problems

CO₂ emissions

Europe's CO_2 emissions averaged 8.5 tonnes per person in 1995 (global average 3.9, USA 20.5, Norway 16.7, UK 9.3, Japan 9.0, Hungary 5.5, Russia 12.2, Mexico 3.9, China 2.7, and Brazil 1.6 (World Resources Institute 1998). Fossil fuels are expected to meet 95% of additional global energy demand between 1995 and 2020; unless new policies are put in place, CO_2 emissions could rise by 70% during this period (International Energy Agency 1999).

Road transportation

This single sector accounts for one-quarter of all CO_2 emitted in Europe with its 37% of the world's car fleet. In addition, vehicle exhaust is often the dominant ingredient in urban air pollution. The estimated costs of adverse environmental and health effects of transport total £185 billion in the European Union (Maddison *et al.* 1996; World Health Organization 1998). Traffic-related air pollution in France, Austria and Switzerland is directly linked to 20 000 deaths annually (Kunzli *et al.* 1999).

Agriculture

Europe is self-sufficient in food, supplies being in equilibrium between imports and exports. However, heavily meat-based diets mean that Europe consumes grain, via livestock as feed, in amounts that are not only unhealthy but prevent Europe from becoming a significant exporter to countries lacking grain in the developing world. Europe's consumption thus causes repercussions extending far beyond its borders.

Food production shows little potential for expansion, given that current agronomic inputs (notably fertilizer and water) are approaching their limits of productivity. The region will probably require more grain if its less affluent sectors continue with a greater emphasis on meat and dairy products. Several countries, notably Poland, Hungary, Romania and Ukraine could expand their grain exports if they adopted economic policies to realize their full agricultural potential. The same could eventually apply to Russia, although its 1998 grain harvest decreased by 29% from that in 1997 because of severe heat, drought and economic mismanagement (Brown *et al.* 1999).

Moreover, Europe's agriculture is an industrialized form of food production, being based on fossil fuels for machinery, fertilizers and pesticides. Intensive cultivation leads to soil erosion, pollution from chemical fertilizers and pesticides, biodiversity loss, and decline of landscape amenity. Livestock in Denmark, The Netherlands and several other countries generate significant amounts of methane, a potent greenhouse gas.

Roughly half of the European grain crop is fed to livestock. Over 3 ha of grainlands and pastures are required to produce 1 tonne of beef; this contrasts with only 0.2 ha at most to produce the same weight of grains, pulses or vegetables. Alternatively reckoned, each kilogram of beef requires 5 kg of high-protein feedstuffs, much of it imported from developing countries. Imports of feedstuffs have diverted over 9 Mha of farmland in developing countries from producing more food for domestic use (McLaren *et al.* 1998).

Fisheries

The North Sea mackerel fishery has declined by 80% since the 1960s because of over-harvesting. The herring fishery in the same sea had to be closed between 1987 and 1992, and has not fully recovered. The cod fishery is in danger of collapsing. Further afield, European fishing fleets have caused a decline in fish stocks in coastal waters of West Africa. Were the European Union's fisheries allowed to rebuild, they could eventually yield a further $2.5 billion worth of fish a year (McGinn 1998).

Industrial pollution

One-quarter of Russia's population lives in areas in which pollution concentrations exceed standards by tenfold. Every twentieth death in Hungary is attributed to air pollution, and similar findings apply in Poland and the Czech Republic. In eastern Europe and the European part of the former Soviet Union, four-fifths of water samples from 200 rivers have proved to be dangerously contaminated. The River Vistula is too dirty over much of its length even for industrial use (United Nations Development Programme 1998). Industrial pollution of land in Europe affects 18 Mha (Greenland, this volume).

Opportunities
CO_2 emissions

Coal subsidies have been sharply reduced in Britain, France, Belgium, Spain, Poland and Russia. There is huge scope for Germany to follow suit: it currently subsidizes coal mining to the extent of $80 000 per miner. In the UK, the shift from coal to natural gas for power production has led to an 8% reduction in carbon emissions between 1990 and 1998 (Geller 1999). With respect to fossil fuels as a whole in Europe, there is an urgent need to adjust the skewedness of subsidies. At least ten times more subsidies go to support fossil fuels than to clean and renewable sources of energy. If all subsidies for fossil fuels were to be eliminated, as should surely be done in view of their environmental externalities, many clean and renewable sources, notably solar energy and wind power, would become commercially competitive (Myers & Kent 1998).

Road transportation

Car sharing networks now comprise more than 100 000 participants in 230 cities. One group in Germany estimates that each of its vehicles replaces five private cars; altogether the fleet eliminates well over 500 000 km of driving each year. Meeting the full market potential of car sharing would eliminate six million cars from European cities.

The Netherlands has one of the highest car densities in the world, yet 30% of urban trips are made by bicycle (in the USA, 1%). In the UK, each car takes up as much road space as eight bicycles and as much parking space as 20 bicycles. In Luneborg, Germany, traffic restraints and improved public transportation have cut car use by 15%, increased bicycle use by 59%, and walking by 48%, whereas serious traffic accidents have been cut by 13.5% (Royal Commission on Environmental Pollution 1994).

There is much scope for more efficient cars. The UK government plans for a 40% improvement in new cars' fuel efficiency over 1990 levels by 2005. Research in the USA and Europe reveals that in a conventional car with its weight and inefficient engine, 95% of energy moves the car and only 5% moves the driver. A 'hypercar', already well advanced in its design process, will have a superlight, low-drag carbon-fibre body, safer than steel, plus a gas turbine or fuel cell for constant electricity, and variable-speed reversible electric motors to capture braking energy. It will be 95% less polluting because of its constant-speed engine and will get 100/200 miles per gallon (Hawken *et al*. 1999).

Road transportation is a leading source of CO_2 emissions. In the UK, cutting CO_2 emissions by 25% from 1990 levels by 2010 would reduce CO_2 emissions by 147 million tonnes, or 2.5 tonnes per person. The government target is a 20% reduction by 2010 (McLaren *et al*.1998).

Cutting waste

In Germany, anti-packaging laws have reduced packaging by 17% since 1991 and increased the recycling rate from 12% to 86%, at a cost of $20 per year per German resident. France, Belgium and Austria have adopted similar legislation. Twelve countries are planning similar take-back measures for electronic goods such as television sets. In Germany again, the Blue Angel Eco-label has been awarded to almost 1000 manufacturers for 4100 products in 76 categories.

The Netherlands has set a national goal for waste reduction of 70–90%. In Denmark, high deposits on refillable glass bottles have yielded a 99% return rate, implying that bottles could be reused as many as 100 times. Also in Denmark, landfill taxes have boosted the reuse of construction debris from 12% to 82% in only eight years, far ahead of the 4% rate of most industrialized countries (Brown *et al*. 1999).

Biodegradable materials made from plant starches, oils and enzymes already replace synthetics and eliminate toxic wastes. Enzymes have replaced phosphates in 90% of all detergents in Europe.

'Industrial ecology'

In Denmark, the Kalundborg industrial park is a blueprint for 'industrial ecosystems' with its 16 materials-exchange and energy-exchange processes. An oil refinery employs waste heat from a power plant and provides sulphur to a wallboard producer. At the same time, the power plant supplies steam to heat water for aquaculture, and warms greenhouses and homes. The complex has greatly reduced its use of oil, coal and water, as well as its emissions of carbon dioxide and sulphur dioxide. The integral strategy has translated into US$120 million in savings and revenues on a US$60 million investment over a five-year period.

Organic agriculture

In the UK, organic agriculture increased from a very low base by an annual average of 28% during 1990–95, and by 47% during 1995–96. The sales value has grown from £40 million in 1987 to over £150 million in 1994, including imports from continental Europe. However, the market share is only 0.3%, one of the lowest in Europe. In Austria, increased supports have led to an increase in organic farms from 2000 to 20 000 during the 1990s.

Wind power

Installed wind power is most concentrated in Germany and Denmark, also in the USA and India. In Denmark, 9% of electricity is supplied by wind power (23% in Spain's northern region of Navarre). In the UK, with the largest wind resource in Europe (28 times that of Denmark in only six times as large an area), there is much potential for offshore wind farms, thus avoiding loss of amenity. The government has set a target of 10% of electricity from renewable sources by 2010 (up from 2.6% today). In 1997 BP announced plans to invest $1 billion and Shell $500 million in wind power and other renewables.

Future strategies

There is huge scope for resource efficiencies, and also for economic savings, through eco-technologies available already. We could enjoy twice as much material well-being while using only half as many raw materials and causing only half as much pollution among other forms of waste. This is known as the 'Factor Four' strategy, and has been espoused by the governments of Austria, The Netherlands and Norway, and also the European Commission. According to the OECD, the governments of Austria and Sweden, as well as the World Business Council for Sustainable Development, we should anticipate a 'Factor Ten' strategy. After all, to achieve sustainable economies we need to reduce our materials and energy intensity (the amount used per unit product) by 50% worldwide. Given that developing countries will be reluctant, even if able, to do so for a while to come, developed nations should aim at cutting theirs by 90%—hence the rationale for Factor Ten (Hinterberger & Schmidt-Bleek 1999). The prospect is not as impracticable as it might sound. After all, labour productivity expanded by a factor of at least 20 in the first half century of the Industrial Revolution, mainly by substituting machinery and commercial energy for human muscle (Hawken *et al.* 1999).

Technologies needed and eminently plausible include: diodes that emit light for twenty years without bulbs; ultrasound washing machines that use no water, heat or soap; deprintable and reprintable paper; plastics that are both reusable and compostable; roofs and roads that do double duty as solar energy collectors; extra-light materials stronger than steel; and quantum semiconductors that store vast amounts of information on chips no bigger than a dot (Hawken *et al.* 1999). Fortunately, too, there is a shortening of the time it takes for advances in technology to reach the marketplace. In the USA, electricity was taken up by one-quarter of the population in 46 years; the telephone needed 35 years; the microwave oven 30 years; television 26 years; radio 22 years; the personal computer 16 years; the mobile phone 13 years; and the world wide web 7 years (United Nations Development Programme 1998).

Europeans could meet their present consumption demands with 10% fewer consumer goods and services, produced with 10% fewer materials, in turn produced with 10% fewer inputs and extracted 10% more efficiently. Many more opportunities will be found in subsequent papers in this volume.

The role of the scientist and technologist is to define options for society by the further elucidation of specific questions. These could include:

- What is the role played by consumption on estimates of the planet's carrying capacity? Although many scientists agree that carrying capacity is one of the most important of all contemporary concepts, there is scant consensus on what it encompasses, especially in operational senses and as applied to communities of various levels of affluence (or poverty). Has humanity already exceeded the Earth's carrying capacity in ways that impose irreversible injury on not only critical resource stocks and environmental services but also on systems of social organization?
- What are the relative impacts of population growth and adverse technology as well as consumption on the environment? How far do the three interact with each other, especially in multiplicative fashion? What indicators can methodically and continuously measure progress towards (or regress from) sustainable consumption?
- What are the economic factors that promote the forms of consumption most harmful to

the environment? These sectors include, notably, power generation, transportation and agriculture.

- What are the repercussions of continuing along a consumption track of business as usual? If humanity does not address the problem of excessive consumption, what will be the concealed costs of inaction? How long, if any time at all, can it afford to wait?
- What is the underlying basis of over-consumption by affluent people? Is it a perceptual hangover from 400 generations since humans came out of their caves, when more of anything has virtually always meant better? Or has it become, in recent times at least, a case of keeping up with the neighbours? Either explanation offers plenty of scope to modify people's preoccupations and preferences, whether within short or long time horizons. How should we move on from 'more is better' to 'enough is best'?

Further clarification is needed of the socio-political driving forces behind consumption. They are not limited to a simple desire to enjoy more goods and services. For instance, there is the impact of changes in the societal infrastructure, as with the trend of rich nations towards smaller households (a consequence of rising divorce rates), which necessitates more dwellings and domestic equipment. Another driving force lies with big-city roads that oblige people to drive cars and will thus delay a shift in this entrenched consumption pattern. In a broader sense, the way in which society is organized often prevents people from making consumption decisions that serve their true needs. It is necessary to know more about all barriers to change, be they economic, institutional, political or policy barriers—and how they can be reduced by fiscal incentives and disincentives (e.g. a carbon tax), or subsidies for renewable and non-polluting energy sources and for public transportation.

Policy options

The above raises profound implications for policy. Plainly, consumption patterns and trends must be modified with all urgency—which will mark a distinct departure from the past, when it has been generally assumed that consumption is beneficial in itself, virtually by definition. The principal goal is to move toward sustainable consumption. This generalized purpose can be divided into four conceptual categories:

1. To devise ways to meet needs that are not so tightly bound to consumption of conventional types.
2. To develop consumption goods and services that are less harmful to the environment.
3. To change forms of consumption from wasteful forms (e.g. junk mail) to more useful materials.
4. To consume in more selective and discriminating fashion—which will often, though not always, mean to consume less.

To indicate the scope for policy interventions of exceptional leverage and with multiplier effects, consider 'perverse' subsidies, or subsidies that are harmful to both our environments and economies. In just the agriculture sector, European Union subsidies are so large that they promote, albeit unwittingly, soil erosion, nitrogen pollution, pesticide damage, biodiversity losses and amenity decline—all to grow crops that are in excess production anyway (Myers & Kent 1998). Agricultural subsidies in OECD countries are more than $300 billion a year: compare this with the funding for international centres working on agricultural research targeted on problems of the poor: less than $350 million (Shah & Strong 1999).

Even more important are fundamental limitations of the marketplace. At a time when the marketplace ethos is promoted as a prime mode of resolving our problems, we should bear in mind that marketplace deficiencies constitute a central problem, notably in the form of (i) large-scale and widespread externalities of both environmental and social sorts, (ii) the discount rate, which often implies there is no future worth considering beyond a few years, and (iii) the issue of property rights with respect to common property resources such as the atmosphere, the oceans and other major non-owned resources. These deficiencies, like subsidies, send resounding messages to the public that it is quite acceptable to continue consuming along present patterns, as if with complete disregard for sustainability. Such pivotal issues are dealt with at various places in the papers that follow; they offer much scope for policy correctives.

In addition, we need to devise a more accurate indicator for the overall health of our economies. The onwards-and-upwards rise of gross domestic product (GDP) presumes that the more that Europeans spend, the better their lives become. However, GDP makes no distinction between desirables and undesirables, only between more and less. Road accidents, crime, diseases and other factors adverse to human welfare are considered to add billions of Euros to our economies, and GDP calls this 'growth'. We need to use more realistic measures of well-being than GDP, through for example an Index of Sustainable Economic Welfare. During the period 1980–96 the UK's GDP rose by over one-third, whereas sustainable economic welfare actually declined by as much as one-fifth (Jackson *et al.* 1997).

Increasingly, millions of Europeans are engaged in an effort to consume less. They are trying to eat less, drink less, smoke less, gamble less—even to spend less generally. Fully one-quarter of Europeans consider themselves overweight; GDP includes both the billions of Euros that they spend on food that they wish they did not eat, and the billions of Euros that they spend on diet and weight-loss schemes. It adds the further billions spent on obesity-related health problems.

Conclusion

An ultimate imperative should be borne in mind. It is not that consumption levels, and hence resource exploitation and pollution levels, should alter (not necessarily decline) among rich communities. They will alter if only because the Earth cannot indefinitely support the present consumption loading, let alone future loading. The realistic choice is whether present consumption is changed through greater efficiency, smarter technologies, more equitable sharing, and a start on moderation in consumption—-or whether it changes anyway as environmental and social systems are undermined until they fail, whereupon people will find themselves obliged to modify their consumption behaviour, especially to do more with less. In many respects, the choice is already being made, albeit by default for the most part.

Box 1: China unsustainable
- If each of China's 1.2 billion people were to consume one extra chicken per year and if that chicken were to be raised primarily on grain, this would account for as much grain as all the grain exports of Canada, the second largest exporter.
- If China's consumption of beef per person, currently only 4 kg per year, were to match the USA's 45 kg, and if the additional beef were produced mainly in feedlots, this would take grain equivalent to the entire US harvest, less than one-third of which is exported.
- If China were to consume seafood at Japan's rate per person, it would need 100 million tonnes, more than today's total catch.
- If China were to match the USA for car ownership and oil consumption per person, it would need more than today's global output of oil, and its cars would emit roughly as much CO_2 as all the world's transportation today.
- If the Chinese were to consume wood products at the Japanese rate, their demand would exceed Japan's nine times over.
- China's economic growth rate has long averaged *ca.* 10% per year. However, environmental problems are taking 8–15% off GDP.

(Sources: Brown 1995; Smil & Yushi 1998.)

References

Brown, L.R. 1995 *Who will feed China? Wake-up call for a small planet*. New York: Norton.

Brown, L.R. and 12 others 1999 *Beyond Malthus: nineteen dimensions of the population challenge*. New York: Norton.

Ehrlich, P.R. & Ehrlich, A.H. 1996 *The betrayal of science and reason: how anti-environmental rhetoric threatens our future*. Washington, DC: Island Press.

Engelman, R. & LeRoy, P. 1995 *Conserving land: Population and sustainable food production*. Washington, DC: Population Action International.

Geller, H. 1999 *Policies for a more sustainable energy future*. Washington, DC: American Council for an Energy-Efficient Economy.

Hawken, P., Lovins, A.B. & Lovins, L.H. 1999 *Natural capitalism*. London: Earthscan.

Hinterberger, F. & Schmidt-Bleek, F. 1999 Dematerialization, MIP and Factor 10: physical sustainability indicators as a social device. *Ecological Economics* **29**, 53–56.

International Energy Agency 1999 *World energy outlook*. Paris: International Energy Agency.

Jackson, T., Laing, F., MacGillivray, A., Marks, N., Ralls, J. & Stymne, S. 1997 *An index of sustainable economic welfare for the UK 1950–1996*. Surrey: Centre for Environmental Strategy, University of Surrey.

Kates, R.W., Chen, R.S., Downing, T.E., Kasperson, J.X., Messer, E. & Millman, S.R. 1988 *The hunger report: 1988*. Rhode Island: World Hunger Program, Brown University.

Kunzli, N., Kaiser, R., Medina, S., Studnicka, G., Oberfield, G. & Horack, F. 1999 *Air pollution attributable cases: health costs due to road traffic related air pollution*. (Paper prepared for WHO Ministerial Conference on Environment and Health, London, June 1999). Geneva: World Health Organization.

McGinn, A. 1998 *Rocking the boat*. Washington, DC: Worldwatch Institute.

McLaren, D., Bullock, S. & Yousuf, N. 1998 *Tomorrow's world*. London: Earthscan.

Maddison, D., Pearce, D., Johansson, O., Calthop, E., Litman, T. & Verhoef, E. 1996 *Blueprint 5: The true costs of road transport*. London: Earthscan.

Meadows, D.H., Meadows, D.L. and Randers, J. 1992 *Beyond the limits*. Post Mills, Vermont: Chelsea Green Publishing.

Millman, S.R. 1991 *The hunger report update*. Rhode Island: World Hunger Program, Brown Unversity.

Myers, N. & Kent, J. 1998 *Perverse subsidies: tax $s undercutting our economies and environments alike*. Winnipeg: International Institute for Environment and Development.

Myers, N. & Kent, J. 2000 *The new consumers: report to the Winslow Foundation*, Washington DC (in preparation).

Pimentel, D., Harvey, C., Resosudarmo, P., Sinclair, K., Kurz, D., McNair, M., Crist, S., Shpritz, L., Fitton, L., Saffouri, R. & Blair, R. 1995 Environmental and economic costs of soil erosion and conservation benefits. *Science* **267**, 1117–1123.

Pimentel, D., Bailey, O., Kim, P., Mullaney, E., Calabrese, J., Walman, L., Nelson, F. & Yao, X. 1999 Will limits of the Earth's resources control human numbers? *Environment, Development and Sustainability* **1**, 19–39.

Postel, S.L., Daily, G.C. & Ehrlich, P.R. 1996 Human appropriation of renewable fresh water. *Science* **271**, 785–788.

Royal Commission on Environmental Pollution 1994 *Transport and the environment*. London: HMSO.

Shah, M. & Strong, M. 1999 *Food in the 21st century: from science to sustainable agriculture*. Washington, DC: CGIAR, The World Bank.

Smil, V. & Yushi, M. 1998 *The economic costs of China's environmental degradation*. Boston: American Academy of Arts and Sciences.

United Nations Development Programme 1998 *Human development report 1998*. New York: Oxford University Press.

World Health Organization 1998 *Health and environment in sustainable development: five years after the Earth Summit*. Geneva: World Health Organization.

World Resources Institute 1998 *World resources report 1998–99*. New York: Oxford University Press.

European biodiversity in the context of sustainable consumption

David Duthie

Biodiversity Planning Support Programme, UNEP, PO Box 47074, Gigiri, Nairobi, Kenya

Europe's biodiversity—a victim of unsustainable development?

The historical landscape of Europe has been transformed by humans. This change has occurred at different scales and rates since the Neolithic period, and has resulted in a dramatic alteration in Europe's biodiversity. Through the Middle Ages and after the Industrial Revolution, progressively more land was converted for agricultural and urban development. Since the end of World War II, the pace of biodiversity loss has increased across much of Europe, primarily as a result of the intensification of agricultural practices. The driving force behind this transformation has been a spectacular increase in human economic activity that few would consider to be sustainable, especially when viewed from the perspective of long-term maintenance of natural capital in the form of biodiversity (Arrow *et al.* 1995). There is increasing evidence that the long-term fate of much of Europe's biodiversity will be decided, irreversibly, by decisions taken (or not taken) within the next 20 years, which will determine the pattern and scale of consumption, both within Europe and throughout the rest of the world (Vitousek *et al.* 1997).

In spite of the magnitude of the changes that have (already) occurred to Europe's biodiversity, politicians and bureaucrats still fail to register its significance. This is because total biodiversity is a multi-faceted, complex entity, able to mean 'anything to anyone', as the following definition, from DeLong (1996), demonstrates:

> Biodiversity is an attribute of an area and specifically refers to the variety within and among living organisms, assemblages of living organisms, biotic communities, and biotic processes, whether naturally occurring or modified by humans. Biodiversity can be measured in terms of genetic diversity and the identity and number of different types of species, assemblages of species, biotic communities, and biotic processes, and the amount (e.g., abundance, biomass, cover, rate) and structure of each. It can be observed and measured at any spatial scale ranging from microsites and habitat patches to the entire biosphere.

With this broad definition, it is perfectly possible that some measures of biodiversity can be stable, and even increasing, while total biodiversity is in significant decline. For example, from estimated regional totals of over 100 000 terrestrial animal and 12 500 plant species, there are thought to have been just 6 animal and 35 plant extinctions across Europe and the CIS since *ca.* 1600 (Smith *et al.* 1993). Many politicians might feel this a price worth paying for the economic development of the continent. However, when measured in other ways, the scale of the loss of biodiversity in Europe is already marked (see figure 1). For

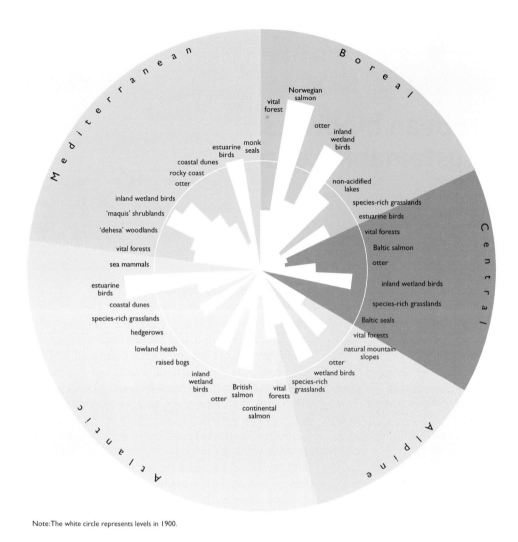

Note: The white circle represents levels in 1900.

*Figure 1. The decline of biodiversity in Europe. (Source: EEA/RIVM (1992),
cited in Stanners & Bourdeau (1995).)*

example, less than 1% of old-growth forest remains; most of the semi-natural grassland in Europe has been destroyed since 1950; there has been a greater than 50% loss of fungal species diversity from sites across much of Europe; and there has been a 95% decline in the area occupied by rare bumblebees in the UK over the past 30 years. Many similar statistics can be gleaned from the European biodiversity literature.

So far, most human influence on Europe's total biodiversity has been through a massive loss of **local** species **abundance**, with relatively little change in **regional** species **diversity**, *senso stricto*. This loss of local abundance is the result of numerous local population extinctions, with a corresponding loss of genetic diversity (Hughes *et al.* 1997), equivalent to a favourite shirt's becoming threadbare, but still 'intact', until one day it simply falls apart. The applicability of this analogy to the thinning of Europe's biodiversity remains unknown.

The causes of loss of European biodiversity

Historically, the major cause of biodiversity loss in Europe has been habitat loss and fragmentation. This conversion has been so complete that, in many European countries, biodiversity hotspots now occur in human-transformed landscapes (compare English chalk grasslands) rather than natural wilderness. This trend in land conversion has stabilized in northern and central Europe, but continues in the south and east. Current trends will lead to a continuing pattern of agricultural intensification in the northwest and increase in extent in southern and eastern Europe unless present agricultural policies change radically.

During most of this period of transition, most of Europe's biodiversity was not being consumed, in the sense of being a direct target of use. What was being consumed was mostly timber, land area and soil fertility. Some loss of biodiversity has resulted from unsustainable direct consumption; for example, the European beaver has been overexploited through hunting, and sturgeon has been over-harvested from rivers. However, most biodiversity loss has been akin to the fate of the 'innocent bystander' involved in a car crash, an accidental victim of unsustainable development.

The impacts of this rapid development on European biodiversity can be broadly grouped into the following categories: (i) loss of habitat, (ii) habitat fragmentation, (iii) chemical pollution (chronic and acute), (iv) overexploitation, and (v) introduced species. Over the next 100 years, all of these impacts might be overshadowed by the combined effects of global warming, which will force species to track changing 'ecological space' across a mosaic of human-transformed landscapes (Peters & Lovejoy 1992).

Although it is inevitable that some biodiversity must be lost as humans expand their 'footprint' across the continent, it is clear that, to a large extent, the current and future pattern of loss is not a managed process, nor is it clear that there is any kind of equilibrium or endpoint to the process that will be compatible with future human needs and desires.

What is known of the current status of Europe's biodiversity is briefly reviewed below. This is followed by a short assessment of how European present and future consumption patterns might influence this situation.

Europe's biodiversity: overview of selected taxa

Although the biodiversity of Europe is the best known of any in the world, it is remarkable how 'thin' this knowledge base is compared with the information required for effective biodiversity management. The best maps of European biodiversity use less than 3% of all recorded species (187 mammal species, 445 birds, 91 reptiles, 48 amphibians and 2370 flowering plants respectively out of a total of over 100 000 terrestrial and freshwater species). These maps reveal that there is a general increase in biodiversity from north to south across Europe. This trend holds for both species richness and endemism (Humphries *et al.* 1999); it holds in spite of the extensive deforestation of southern Europe that occurred during the times of the Greek and Roman empires.

At least since the last Ice Age, Europe has not been a global hotspot for biodiversity. Nevertheless, Europe does contain some significant biodiversity components, both in terms of wild species and also within a diverse range of agro-ecosystems. An overall summary of Europe's biodiversity is given in Table 1, together with a brief summary of major differences in the conservation requirements of different vertebrate taxa within Europe (country by country data are given in Annex 1).

Table 1. Regional species richness for Europe

(Source: Stanners & Bourdeau (1995).)

taxon	total number	threatened within Europe (%)	endemic to Europe (%)
mammals	*244	42	18
birds	514	15	6
reptiles	199	45	11
amphibians	71	30	20
fish (freshwater)†	358	41	<10
invertebrates‡	§200 000	5	not known
bryophytes‖	1 687	24	13
higher plants	12 500	21	35

Notes: *187 if Russia, Belarus, Ukraine and Moldovia are excluded; †Kottelat (1997); ‡includes marine invertebrates; §estimate; ‖Hodgetts (1996).

Mammals

It is becoming increasingly clear that the long-term conservation of Europe's threatened mammals requires the maintenance of large continuous areas of essentially natural habitat with little or no human influence. The proportion of national mammal species threatened varies across Europe, from *ca.* 50% in Great Britain and France to less than 5% in the former Yugoslavia (it is not known to what extent the recent conflict will have altered this estimate). Large and medium-sized carnivores and omnivores, such as brown bear (*Ursus arctos*), the wolf (*Canis lupus*), the Spanish lynx (*Lynx pardina*), the European mink (*Mustela lutreola*) and the otter (*Lutra lutra*), are increasingly confined to the eastern parts of Europe, although some western and southern populations persist as the result of (expensive) conservation programmes. The loss of large mammal species from many ecosystems is leading to ecological repercussions, such as explosions of deer populations, which require expensive management interventions. Europe has *ca.* 30 species of marine mammals, including some under extreme threat, such as the Mediterranean monk seal (*Monachus monachus*), still one of the ten most endangered mammals in the world after 30 years of conservation action.

Birds

The conservation requirements of European birds are relatively well documented and understood. A total of 195 species (38% of Europe's avifauna) are designated as Species of European Conservation Concern (SPECs) because their populations are small, declining or geographically restricted. A total of 42% of SPECs are the result of agricultural intensification, although a wide range of other threats contribute to the decline of most species. The requirements for bird conservation in Europe make an interesting contrast with those for mammals. Bird diversity in Europe has become more closely associated with low intensity farming systems than has that of mammals: over 50% of Europe's most highly valued biotopes for conservation occur on low-intensity farmland. The future of bird diversity in Europe will be determined not so much by the creation of large-scale protected areas, but rather by the management regimes operating on the agricultural landscape of Europe.

Reptiles and amphibians

The herpetofauna of Europe is also in decline (Gasc *et al.* 1997), primarily as a result of loss of suitable habitat. Luckily, the (size of) area of habitat required, and even its 'naturalness', are not such critical issues in the conservation of reptiles and amphibians as with birds and mammals. However, it is proving to be an essential part of herpetofauna conservation that the connectivity of small habitats is taken into consideration to promote conservation success.

Fishes

The freshwater and migratory fish of Europe are under severe threat from river engineering, over-exploitation and pollution (Kottelat 1997). Pollution with domestic, agricultural and industrial wastes, including acid deposition, is probably the most important factor in the recent decline of most species. Successful conservation of endangered fish species will not be possible until the external (pollution) threat is removed, even if protected areas are created.

Plants

The conservation status of Europe's plants and the need for further protection have been reviewed by Humphries *et al*. (1999). The threats to plant diversity vary across Europe, ranging from acidification in Scandinavia (in Sweden, 20 000 of 90 000 lakes are acidified to some extent, whereas 60% of Europe's commercial forests are affected by sulphur deposition (United Nations Development Programme 1998)), agricultural intensification in western Europe, through to fire, overgrazing and tourism in southern Europe (Stanners & Bourdeau 1995). Increasingly, plant species persist only in small, isolated populations where they will remain susceptible to external pollution impacts and internal effects of demographic, environmental and genetic stochasticity.

Europe's response to the decline of biodiversity

The primary response to loss of biodiversity in Europe has been defensive, focusing on the protection of wildlife in reserves and on programmes for the preservation of particular species. The 'estate' of protected areas in Europe is perhaps the most complex in the world, comprising a bewildering 190 types of area ranging from large Biosphere Reserves to often tiny Sites of Special Scientific Interest (SSSI).

The simplest, and perhaps surest, way to maintain total biodiversity is to allow 'natural systems' to operate independently of humanity's influence. This requires the maintenance of 'wilderness areas' where ecological (even evolutionary) processes can still proceed as though humans were not present. It is unclear what the minimum operational size required for a 'natural system' to maintain itself must be. To some extent, this will be contingent on the type of ecosystem and the timescale used for measuring sustainability, but a reasonable estimate of the areas required to maintain a natural evolving system including large mammalian predators might be 100 000 ha.

In most of Europe, the establishment of wilderness areas of this size is not a realistic option. Few areas remain in Europe where humans' influence is sufficiently small to allow a wilderness designation. In one global study, Europe was estimated to have 15.6% undisturbed land, 19.6% partly disturbed land and 64.9% human-dominated land, making Europe the continental area with the largest human footprint. Most of the undisturbed land remaining is located in the arctic and boreal systems of northern Europe. A recent survey of IUCN Category II protected areas in Europe lists 32 areas of 100 000 ha or more. Category II protected areas (National Parks) are managed mainly for ecosystem conservation and recreation; they are natural areas of land and/or sea, designated to (i) protect the ecological integrity of one or more ecosystems for this and future generations, (ii) exclude exploitation or occupation inimical to the purposes of designation of the areas and (iii) provide a foundation for spiritual, scientific, educational, recreational and visitor opportunities, all of which must be environmentally and culturally compatible. Almost all of these areas in Europe are in Fennoscandian countries or Russia and have relatively low levels of overall diversity and thus can make only a small contribution to the maintenance of Europe's total biodiversity. Those from more southern areas comprise mostly mountainous habitat: there is no lowland wilderness left in Europe!

In the absence of large areas capable of supporting natural evolving systems, the long-term conservation of biodiversity in Europe will require human intervention. Indeed, so old is the human footprint in Europe, much of its biodiversity is already dependent upon human (agricultural) activities. Recent changes in agricultural policy and practices comprise the biggest single threat to Europe's biodiversity at present. On paper, Europe has an extensive network of protected areas, even though the exact number and area are not known, owing to the variety (around 190 types) of categories of protected areas found in different countries. These areas obviously have an important role in biodiversity maintenance, but there are a number of limitations to their effectiveness. Although there are over 2200 protected areas of greater than 1000 ha, covering over 800 000 km^2 (*ca.* 10% of Europe's total land area), more than 50% of this area is Category V (Protected Landscape) rather than Category I—IV (Nature Reserve/National Park) and has limited biodiversity conservation value. Even within Europe's Category II protected areas, there is often legal or illegal exploitation of biodiversity in the form of hunting/poaching, timber extraction and overgrazing, or external influences undermining conservation. Furthermore, the spatial distribution of the existing protected area network in Europe does not reflect the overall distribution of biodiversity: many areas of biodiversity richness lie outside the existing protected area network, especially in southern Europe.

The plethora of initiatives within Europe to expand the network of protected areas and to focus efforts on species with special conservation needs has attempted to address the diverse range of problems facing Europe's biodiversity. A summary of the most important activities is given in Table 2. Although there is little to criticize in the aims and objectives of these programmes, the increased bureaucracy associated with initiatives being discussed and approved at such a high level within European institutions carries a danger of increased delay before urgently needed practical actions are undertaken. For example, the recent 1996 Red List of Threatened Animals lists 145 species of non-marine molluscs as threatened, yet the Bern Convention and Habitats Directive list only 19 and 25 (including the same 19) species respectively (Bouchet *et al.* 1999).

Table 2. The major European biodiversity conservation initiatives

Convention on Wetlands of International Importance Especially as Waterfowl Habitat (Ramsar Convention) (1971)
Man and Biosphere Programme (1971)
Convention concerning the Protection of the World Cultural and Natural Heritage (World Heritage Convention) (1972)
Convention on International Trade in Endangered Species (CITES-Washington Convention) (1973)
European Diploma (1975)
European Network of Biogenetic Reserves (1976)
Convention on the Conservation of Migratory Species of Wild Animals (Bonn Convention) (1979)
Convention on the Conservation of European Wildlife and Natural Habitats (Bern Convention) (1979)
Directive on the Conservation of Wild Birds (Birds Directive) (1979)
Convention on the Protection of the Alps (Alpine Convention) (1991)
Convention on Biological Diversity (1992)
Directive on the Conservation of Natural and Semi-natural Habitats and of Wild Fauna and Flora (Habitats Directive) (1992)
Helsinki Convention on the Protection of the Marine Environment of the Baltic Sea Area (1974, 1992)
Pan-European Biological and Landscape Diversity Strategy (1995)
European Community Biodiversity Strategy (1998)

The most significant change in conservation policy in Europe in recent years has been the (albeit slow) incorporation of environmental considerations into the sectoral policy of the European Union, for example the designation of Environmentally Sensitive Areas (ESAs). Although these have yet to achieve a major influence, incentives for the use of environmentally friendly farming techniques, such as direct drilling, fallowing, and leaving crop stubble, as well as research into precision agriculture and the use of perennial crops, hold great promise for the future.

Sustainable development, consumption and biodiversity

Sustainable use of biodiversity is still a controversial part of the overall conservation system in Europe. Although it is clear that sustainable forestry, hunting, multiple use and tourism, for example, all have the potential to increase the value of 'natural' habitats, there are few examples of long-term sustainability from such uses. Some marine resources, such as pilot whales around the Faroes Islands, are exploited in an apparently sustainable manner, even if the practice is deeply unpopular with animal welfare groups.

Recently, much has been made of the idea that the salvation of biodiversity lies in improved capture of the estimated economic value of biodiverse resources (Costanza *et al.* 1997). In the European environment, much of the value of 'ecosystem services' is, in fact, associated with systems with relatively low diversity. Capturing the economic value of these benefits and transferring them to the protection of high-diversity locations represents a difficult challenge for conservation planners.

There is now a general consensus about the definition of sustainable development as being 'meeting the needs of the present without compromising the ability of future generations to meet their own needs' (World Commission on Environment and Development 1987). To achieve this, it is necessary to 'keep capital intact'. Strong sustainability has a requirement that each of three different forms of capital (natural, human and human-made) is maintained intact or increased independently. Weak sustainability would allow substitution between forms of capital, so long as overall total capital remained intact or increased.

It is patently clear that, in Europe, natural capital is not being maintained intact; this applies especially to the biodiversity component of natural capital. The clearest indications of the depletion of natural capital come from assessments of human appropriation of net primary production (NPP) and calculations of human ecological footprints. These techniques have recently been applied to parts of Europe: The Netherlands, Austria and the Baltic drainage basin. Footprint analyses reveal that centres of high population density require the collection of resources from areas much greater than the centre itself (Wackernagel, this volume).

While human interference in natural systems remains at this intensity, it is clear that overall biodiversity will continue to decline, partly as the result of direct consumption, but mostly as the result of the erosion of ecosystem integrity.

There is considerable scope for intensive conservation management to slow the rate of, and even reverse, this decline through improved networking of existing and new protected areas, through sustainable forestry management (Nilsson, this volume) and improved agricultural land use practices (Greenland, this volume). However, unless the driving forces that promote unsustainable economic growth, such as the Common Agricultural Policy, are revised, it is unlikely that intensification of conservation effort will be able to 'keep up' with the ongoing erosion of biodiversity.

References

Arrow, K. and 10 others 1995 Economic growth, carrying capacity, and the environment. *Science* **268**, 520–521.

Bouchet, P., Falkner, G. & Seddon, M.B. 1999 Lists of protected land and freshwater molluscs in the Bern Convention and European Habitats Directive: are they relevant to conservation? *Biological Conservation* **90**, 21–31.

Costanza, R. and 12 others 1997 The value of the world's ecosystem services and natural capital. *Nature* **387**, 253–260.

DeLong, D.C. 1996 Defining biodiversity. *Wildlife Society Bulletin* **24**, 738–749.

Gasc, J.-P. and 13 others (eds.) 1997 *Atlas of amphibians and reptiles in Europe*. Paris: Societas Europaea Herpetologica and Muséum National d'Histoire Naturelle (IEGB/SPN).

Hodgetts, N.G. 1996 Threatened bryophytes in Europe. *Anales del Instituto de Biologia Universidad Nacional Autonoma de Mexico Serie Botanica* **67**(1), 183–200.

Hughes, J., Daily, G.C. & Ehrlich, P.R. 1997 Population diversity: its extent and extinction. *Science* **278**, 689–692.

Humphries, C., Araujo, M., Williams, P., Lampinen, R., Lahti, T. & Uotila, P. 1999 Plant diversity in Europe: Atlas Florae Europaeae and WORLDMAP. *Acta Botanica Fennica* **162**, 11–21.

Kottelat, M. 1997 European freshwater fishes. A heuristic checklist of the freshwater fishes of Europe (exclusive of former USSR), with an introduction for non-systematists and comments on nomenclature and conservation. *Biologia* **52** (Suppl. 5), 1–271.

Peters, R.L. & Lovejoy T.E. (eds) 1992 *Global warming and biological diversity*. New Haven: Yale University Press.

RIVM (National Institute of Public Health and Environmental Protection) 1992 *The environment of Europe: a global perspective*. Bilthoven, Netherlands: National Institute of Public Health and Environment Protection.

Smith, F.D.M., May, R.M., Pellew, R., Johnson, T.H. & Walter, K.R. 1993 How much do we know about the current extinction rate? *Trends in Ecology and Evolution* **8**(10), 375–378.

Stanners, D. & Bourdeau, P. (eds) 1995 *Europe's environment: the Dobris assessment*. Copenhagen: European Environment Agency.

Vitousek, P.M., Mooney, H.A., Lubchenco, J. & Melillo, J.M. 1997 Human domination of Earth's ecosystems. *Science* **277**, 494–499.

World Commission on Environment and Development 1987 *Our common future*. New York: Oxford University Press.

Annex 1. Species richness and conservation threat by European country

(S, number of species; T, number of species threatened. Source: Stanners and Bourdeau (1995).)

country	mammals		birds		reptiles		amphibians		fish		invertebrates		vascular plants	
	S	T	S	T	S	T	S	T	S	T	S	T	S	T
Albania	63		215		31		13						3965	
Austria	82	32	219	78	14	12	21	19	73	31	>30000		2873	857
Belarus	70	14	208	75	7		2		58	5	10000	85	1720	156
Belgium	58	14	169	49	8	6	17	17			42000		1415	340
Bulgaria	78	8	358	57	36	7	16	1	65	15			3583	770
Cyprus	20	14	357	12	27	25.9	5			0.0			1760	61
Czech Republic	87	26	220	62	13	8	20	13	65	4	27000	94	2500	507
Denmark	43	12	170	22	5	0	14	4	33	6	3760	498	1200	117
Estonia	66	13	316	73	5	1	10	4	76	9	27000		1560	155
Finland	62	7	234	16	5	1	5	1	60	7	18499	148	1350	100
France	89	58	353	132	36	18	30	15	75	17	67500		4700	142
Germany (E)	75	28	220	68	8	5	19	11	51	20			2100	510
Germany (W)	100	41	273	108	13	10	19	13	70	46			2728	664
Greece	88	57	407	100	57	7	16	1	106	21			4900	102
Hungary	73	14	346	41	15	4	15	1	81	2	41460	204	2411	154
Iceland	12		75	5			0		5	1	1245		383	13
Ireland	26	0	141	11	1		3	1	26	6			815	159
Italy	88	31	230	100	51	13	33	8	56	10	57300	2308	6190	737
Latvia	60	26	308	72	7	3	11	5	76	25			1658	277
Lithuania	65	18	308	67	8	1	12	4	76	3			1609	248
Luxembourg	56	33	280	54	7	6	15	13	38	13	30000		1200	153
Malta	21	28	46.4		8		1						900	4
Netherlands	55	19	180	60	7	7	16	10	34	27	27700		1436	497
Norway	55	4	249	23	5	1	5	2	41	2	20000	47	1310	87
Poland	83	11	222	31	8	2	18	1	66	7	28384	389	2300	196
Portugal	66	9	311	41	34	3	17	28	8				3150	118
Romania	86		249		25	19							3350	
Slovak Republic	43	28	235	68	12	10	17	12	61	15			2500	893
Soviet Union (former)	354	94	803	80	37		9			9	204		21000	603
Spain	82	20	327	38	55	10	25	2	68	16	25000	391	8000	485
Sweden	58	12	242	19	6		13	6	45	5	23400	421	1900	165
Switzerland	74	22	204	83	15	11	20	16	53	20	45400	15713	2696	579
Turkey	81	45	426	46	100	23	18	7	175	17		19	8494	1944
Ukraine		29		28	6		4					18		146
United Kingdom	49	20	520	147		6	33.3	6	34	7	33.3		1494	154
Yugoslavia (former)	97	3	245	17	41	1	23	2		5				5273

Land resources

Dennis J. Greenland

Department of Social Science, University of Reading, Whiteknights, Reading RG6 2DW, UK

Introduction: defining land consumption

Land is consumed by the advance of the oceans, by degradation associated with soil erosion and the natural reshaping of the landscape through weathering of the rocks, and the subsequent action of wind and water. The natural processes can be greatly accelerated by the actions of man, associated with agricultural practices, deforestation and mining activities, but the alienation of land for urban, industrial and related purposes can also reduce its productivity and value as a source of food, fibre and fuel, biodiversity, natural beauty, and amenity uses, although urbanization can at the same time increase its economic value. The question of the carrying capacity of the land in terms of the human population that can be supported has exercised the minds of many. Although others preceded him, the essay of Thomas Malthus 'On the principle of population as it affects the future improvement of society' written 200 years ago is best known in Europe for formulating the problem of the conflict between the geometric rate of expansion of population and the arithmetic growth in the ability of land to produce food.

Malthus invoked many examples of the miseries that arose where population density exceeded the ability of the land to support those living there, notably in China, in the early nineteenth century. There have been more recent examples, as in Rwanda, formerly the most densely populated country in Africa, where conflicts over land, and the inability of the land to support the growing population, have been the underlying reason for genocide on an extraordinary scale.

In more general terms, however, Malthus' theorizing has largely been proved wrong. This has been because scientific advances in methods to improve the productivity of the land have enabled food production to grow at a rate equal to population growth. Only where economic and political forces have prevented the application of scientific advances to agriculture, as in many parts of Africa, has food production fallen below the rate of population increase. The growth of population in Europe can be traced in relation to the evolution of methods to enhance the productivity of the land. These methods have included land drainage, liming, manuring and other practices initiated some 2000 years ago, and the introduction in the nineteenth century of the use of farm machinery and inorganic fertilizers. These practices, as well as the improvement of crops, ensured that the relatively slow increase in the population of Europe before 1800 and the very much more rapid growth since then not only has been supported but has led to production in excess of demand, so that farmers are now paid to set aside land from agricultural production.

The important question is whether this increase in production has been achieved without 'consuming' the land and reducing its ability to serve the needs and desires of present and future populations, or the resources required to produce the inputs of fertilizers and other products needed to sustain the yields required.

The amount of food produced is a product of the area of land cultivated and the yield obtained

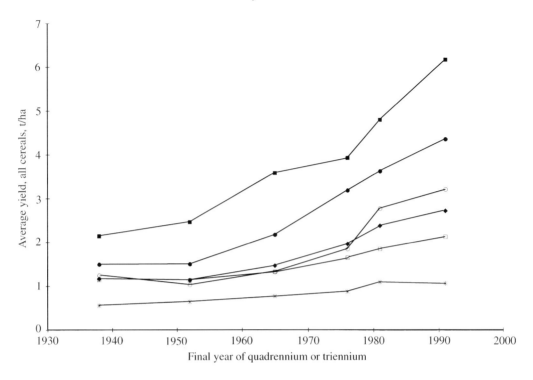

Figure 1. Average cereal yields in Europe compared with other regions and the world. Symbols: filled squares, UK; filled circles, Europe; filled diamonds, the world; stars, Africa; open circles, Asia; open squares, Latin America and the Caribbean. (Data from FAO Production Year Books.)

from that land. In Europe almost all of the increase in production has been obtained without increasing the area of land used for agriculture. This is true of the world as a whole since 1975 but is not true of Africa. The increases in cereal yields between 1963 and 1990, the period of the so-called 'green revolution,' although usually considered to be a feature of the more favoured developing countries, were in fact greater in several European countries than in Asia (Figure 1). In few countries in Africa did yields increase, and in some they fell. These data indicate that the quality of land resources as far as the ability to sustain food production is concerned have increased substantially in Europe, and to a slightly smaller extent in most of Asia, but in many countries in Africa they have fallen. Even in those countries in Africa where there has been an increase in yields, the increases were small and not commensurate with the greater inputs that have been used in an attempt to increase yields.

The question now facing Europe is how far cereal yields can be further improved without damaging the environment. The yield limits set by radiation and temperature and atmospheric CO_2 concentration are still well above the average European cereal yields of 4—6 t ha^{-1}. However, the amounts of fertilizer or manure required to attain these levels are such that pollution of water resources becomes a real threat, so that the European Union Nitrates Directive 1991 (effective from 1999) has been framed to control the net supply of nitrogen to the soil. Analyses of the problem of balancing food production and environmental issues in Europe have been given by Rabbinge *et al.* (1994) and the European Environment Agency (1999). By improving land quality its value is increased, and the high-yield techniques are 'land-saving' because they reduce the need to use more easily degraded land for agriculture. However, whereas land might not be consumed, the resources needed to maintain the high yields are.

Consumption of resources used to increase land productivity in Europe

Over the course of centuries, huge investments have been made in the lands of Europe to improve drainage, to prevent flooding, to irrigate the land in times of drought, to ensure accessibility to the land through the building of roads, and to prevent erosion of the land by wind or water. These investments have not only ensured that land use is sustainable but have also greatly increased its existing and potential productivity. However, the value of the land is determined not only by the investments made in it but also by its inherent properties. Europe is fortunate that much of the land is of good quality and is either resistant to degradation or has a high resilience so that it can recover readily from various stresses associated with different forms of land use (Greenland & Szabolcs 1994). Much of Europe is also favoured by suitable climates for crop production, so that the potential of the land can be realized, provided that appropriate inputs are used.

These inputs include lime to prevent acidification, fertilizers or manures to replace nutrients removed, and organic manures to maintain the physical and biological condition of the soil. Acidification arises from several causes. Leaching of calcium and magnesium from the soil by rain is a natural phenomenon causing acidification, but it can be accelerated if the rain has been further acidified by industrial gases. Removal of calcium and magnesium in crops can similarly lead to acidification. Liming of the land is then necessary both to correct acidity and to return the calcium and sometimes the magnesium that has been removed. The organic acids that are leached from the leaves of coniferous trees also are active in causing acidification, because of their ability to remove not only calcium and magnesium from the soil but also iron and other heavy-metal cations. Fortunately, as has been known from pre-Roman times, acidity can be readily corrected by the use of chalk and chalky soil, both of which are abundant, and liming and marling have been part of good farming practices for centuries.

The nutrients required by plants are sufficient in many European soils to sustain moderate crop yields for many years. However, they are inadequate to produce or sustain yields greater than a few tonnes per hectare. To produce and sustain yields of the order of 5 or 6 t ha^{-1}, which is the current average European wheat yield and is the level needed to maintain the present food prices, most soils require substantial inputs of fertilizer. A crop of 6 tonnes of wheat removes in the grain approximately 120 kg of nitrogen, 25 kg of phosphorus, 35 kg of potassium, 4 kg of calcium, 9 kg of magnesium and 9 kg of sulphur, plus much smaller quantities of micronutrients. If the soil is not to be degraded, these must be replaced, together with losses due to other processes. These loss processes usually mean that the efficiency with which nutrients are recovered from fertilizers is often less than 50%, so that the quantities of nutrients applied must be at least twice these levels. Depending on the formulation of the fertilizer used, this means that amounts of fertilizer of the order of 1 t ha^{-1} must be applied. Fertilizer use in Europe over the past 50 years has almost certainly exceeded removals, so that a reserve has been established in many soils. Recent reductions in the amounts used have therefore had little effect on productivity, while reducing the polluting effects of the nutrients not absorbed by crops. This can be contrasted with the severe mining of nutrients and depletion of soil fertility that has been taking place in Africa (Stoorvogel & Smaling 1990). The use of organic manures instead of inorganic fertilizers to maintain the nutrient supplies in the soil has both advantages and disadvantages. Poultry and cattle manure can contain as much as 40 kg of nitrogen per tonne dry mass, and 20 kg of phosphorus and a similar amount of potassium per tonne, as well as other nutrients. More generally the nutrient contents of organic manures are considerably less. Thus over 3 tonnes dry mass, or over 10 tonnes wet mass, are needed to maintain nutrient levels if yields of the order of 6 t ha^{-1} are to be obtained. This assumes that similar recoveries of *ca.* 50% of the total nutrients contained are harvested in crops. There is a significantly larger energy cost in collecting and distributing these weights of organic manures. Nevertheless, there are other advantages in the use of organic manures, notably their importance in sustaining biological activity in the soil, and contributing to the physical stability of the soil.

The importance of soil organic matter to land quality and productivity has been a matter of considerable debate. The Rothamsted experiments in the UK have now been continued for more than 150 years, and have compared yields of wheat after treatments with high levels of inorganic fertilizers with those obtained from plots treated with 35 tonnes of farmyard manure per hectare. Although the organic matter content of the soil treated with farmyard manure increased to more than three times the level in the plots receiving only inorganic fertilizers, the yields from the plots treated with inorganic fertilizers became greater than those on the plots receiving farmyard manure, and this difference was reversed only after 100 years when the nitrogen applied in the plots receiving farmyard manure was boosted with nitrogen from inorganic fertilizers to make the amounts added on both plots equal. The organic manured plots had to receive an additional 92 kg of nitrogen per hectare. The fact that the plots that have now received very heavy dressings of inorganic fertilizers for over 150 years continue to produce high crop yields is good evidence that, at least on some soils, such treatments do not necessarily harm the soil. However, over the past 25 years, when the yields of wheat harvested from both treatments have exceeded 6 t ha^{-1}, the yields from the plots receiving farmyard manure supplemented with inorganic nitrogen fertilizer have become slightly greater than those from the plots receiving only inorganic fertilizers (Johnston 1994). The small difference (less than 1 t ha^{-1}) can be attributed to the effects of the organic manures on the physical and biological properties of the soil. Other long-term experiments conducted in developing countries have shown the importance of use of organic manures with inorganic fertilizers if yields are to be sustained (Greenland 1994).

To obtain and maintain the high yields requires not only replacement of nutrients and control of acidity, but also control of fungal and insect pests, and control of weeds. This has been achieved by the use of various chemical pesticides. When it was found that some of these could have adverse effects on organisms other than those targeted, there was a considerable public outcry, and it is still sometimes asserted that the use of chemicals is poisoning the soil. In the course of the past 30 years, the use and management of pesticides, and legislation regarding their use, have greatly improved, and there is no evidence that soil productivity is declining owing to poisoning of the land by pesticides or fertilizers. However, there are secondary effects of the use of high levels of fertilizers and pesticides that must be recognized. These include the pollution of water supplies by nitrates and some pesticides, mostly arising from their improper use.

The consumption of fertilizers is extensive. In 1990 the total worldwide use of inorganic fertilizers was estimated by the Food and Agriculture Organization to be 250 Mt (of N + P$_2$O$_5$ + K$_2$O). The annual use has tended to decrease since then, the largest decreases occurring in developed countries. To feed the growing population of the world it will certainly have to increase substantially in developing countries. Vlek *et al.* (1997) have recently summarized the resources available to sustain this consumption. The only limitation for nitrogen is the energy required at present to convert atmospheric nitrogen to ammonium. At present this is considerable but, as many nitrogen-fixing organisms have shown, the trick of releasing the energy in the nitrogen triple bond does not necessarily require a large energy input. However, the trick has still to be learnt. Given continued investment in the necessary research, there is no reason to expect that this will be an insuperable scientific problem. Hence it can be expected that the provision of adequate nitrogen supplies will become a sustainable process.

The lowest estimate of phosphorus reserves in known deposits is 3.4 Gt (Vlek *et al.* 1997); other estimates are much greater. The lowest estimate is sufficient to meet current demand for 90–130 years. Nevertheless, greater efficiencies in the use of phosphate to support crop production as demand increases are obviously needed, as well as studies to enable more efficient recycling of phosphorus. Known potassium reserves should be sufficient for a further millennium, and there is no reason to expect that future supplies of other essential nutrients will become limiting within a similar period.

The sustainability of pesticide supplies is also not a problem as far as the availability of natural resources is concerned, but it might be a problem in economic terms. Reducing use by means of integrated pest management systems, in which biological control methods and host plant resistance are combined with pesticide applications, offers a more efficient and therefore more sustainable method of pest management.

Land degradation in Europe

The Global Assessment of Soil Degradation (GLASOD) project (Oldeman *et al.* 1990) indicated that of 287 Mha of agricultural land in Europe, 72 Mha, or 25%, was degraded; of 156 Mha of permanent pasture land, 35% was degraded; and of 353 Mha of forest and woodland, 26% was degraded. The causes are given as deforestation (84 Mha), overgrazing (50 Mha), agricultural activities (64 Mha) and industrial activities (21 Mha). Europe here includes Russia and other countries of the former USSR west of the Urals. The major components of degradation are water erosion, pollution and the physical compaction, sealing and crusting of soils (Table 1). Unfortunately the study did not include estimates of the ease or costs of reversing the degradation, although some of the components were divided into degrees of severity. Of these some of the moderate and all of the severe or extreme examples are difficult or very expensive to reverse.

These assessments were made by scientists in the countries concerned, on the basis of a standard format (Oldeman *et al.* 1990) and soil maps of the countries. They are subjective assessments that nevertheless give an indication of the present extent and severity of the land degradation problem, although no indication of the rate at which degradation is advancing. The total area of degraded land in Europe (211 Mha) refers to 1985–88. The United Nations' 1998 Human Development Report (see Matthews & Hammond 1997) gives a slightly higher figure (219 Mha). The figures in the final column of Table 1 were obtained on the assumption that all of the severe and extreme degradation was occurring on the agricultural or arable land. Some of the degradation occurs under pasture and forests, but it is rarely extreme, so that the scale of land 'consumption' should be approximated by these figures. The dominant importance of the erosion problem in Africa is readily recognized.

Salinization, mostly associated with inadequately drained irrigated areas, affects 4 Mha in

Table 1. *Components and extent of soil degradation in Europe and Africa* (Data from Oldeman *et al.* (1990).)

		Extent/Mha				
Component/severity		low	moderate	severe extreme	total degraded	severe extreme (% of total arable land)
Continent	Component					
Europe					211.1	
	water erosion	21	81	12	114	4.1
	wind erosion	3	38	1	42	1.5
	pollution	4	14	0.1	18.1	0.5
	salinization	1	2	1	4	0.03
	compaction, sealing and crusting	25	8	0	33	1.2
Africa					446.2	
	water erosion	58	67	102	227	55
	wind erosion	88	89	9	186	4.8
	pollution	—	0.2	—	0.2	0
	salinization	5	8	2	0.1	0.1
	compaction, sealing and crusting	1	8	9	4.8	4.8

Europe. It can be reversed by the installation of drainage facilities and the use of good-quality water, but this can be expensive. The rise in sea-level associated with global warming, which was not considered as part of land degradation in the GLASOD project, might well be the most important source of land consumption in the coming century. However, with early and adequate preparation, as has been instigated in the Netherlands, this can also be averted, although at considerable cost. Industrial pollution of land in Europe affects 18 Mha, which could be as much as 90% of the world total. Again, recovery is generally possible through bioremediation (the use of plant species that absorb the heavy-metal pollutants) or other techniques, but might be very slow or expensive.

Land is also consumed by urban sprawl, industrial development, road building and the associated alienation of land to non-rural uses. There is a lack of good data on rates of consumption of land for urban use (Young 1998). The rate of consumption undoubtedly increases as population density increases. Data from China quoted by Fischer & Heilig (1997) give the amount of land needed when the population density is 35 persons km^{-2} as 1.75% of the land area, and when the density increases to 675 persons km^{-2} as 13.5% of the land. As population tends to grow most rapidly on the best land, this usually means that the best agricultural land is consumed for urban and industrial development. In the UK, buildings cover 10% of the land, and roads and railways 3%. Most of the predicted population increase in the near future will be in urban areas, with little change or decreases in rural areas, so that land alienation will almost certainly become an increasing source of land consumption.

Conclusions

Land is an essential resource for the survival and well-being of people throughout the world. Europe is fortunate in that efforts to improve land productivity have continued for many centuries, so that net productivity has increased, in spite of much alienation of land for urban and industrial use. Much of this success has been associated with security of tenure and the desire of land-owners to pass on the land to their heirs in at least as good a condition as that in which they inherited it. In other parts of the world, where tenure arrangements are less secure, and soils are poorer and climates less favourable, land-users have often degraded their lands, by accelerating the erosion processes and mining their soils of nutrients, until in some parts of the world we are on the brink of the Malthusian precipice, and in a few we have fallen over the brink. Given the political will, and the necessary commitment to education and research, this could be prevented (Greenland *et al.* 1998).

References

European Environment Agency 1999 *Europe's environment: the second assessment.* Copenhagen: European Environment Agency.

Fischer, G. & Heilig, G.K. 1997 Population momentum and the demand on land and water resources. *Phil. Trans. R. Soc. Lond.* B **352**, 869–889.

Greenland, D.J. 1994 Long-term cropping experiments in developing countries: the need, the history and the future. In *Long-term experiments in agricultural and ecological science* (eds R.A. Leigh & A.E. Johnston), pp. 187–210. Wallingford: CAB International.

Greenland, D.J., Gregory, P.J. & Nye, P.H. 1998 Summary and conclusions. In *Land resources: on the edge of the Malthusian precipice?* (eds D.J. Greenland, P.J. Gregory & P.H. Nye), pp. 1–7. Wallingford: CAB International.

Greenland, D.J. & Szabolcs, I. (eds) 1994 *Soil resilience and sustainable land use.* Wallingford: CAB International.

Johnston, A.E. 1994 The Rothamsted Classical Experiments. In *Long-term experiments in agricultural and ecological science* (eds R.A. Leigh & A.E. Johnston), pp. 9–38. Wallingford: CAB International.

Matthews, E. & Hammond, A. 1997 *Natural resource consumption* (background paper for the United Nations' Human Development Report 1998). New York: Oxford University Press.

Oldeman, L.R., Hakkeling, R.T.A. & Sombroek, W.G. 1990 *World map of the status of human-induced soil degradation: an explanatory note.* Wageningen: International Soil Reference and Information Centre; Nairobi: United Nations Environment Programme.

Rabbinge, R., van Diepen, C.A., Dijsselbloem, J., de Koning, G.J.H., van Latensteijn, H.C., Woltjer, E. and van Zijl, J. 1994 Ground for choices: a scenario study on perspectives for rural areas in the European Community. In *Future of the land* (eds L. Fresco, L. Stroosnijder, J.J. Bouma & H. van Keulen), pp. 95–121. Chichester: Wiley.

Stoorvogel, J.J. & Smaling, M.A. 1990 *Assessment of soil nutrient depletion in Africa*. Report 28. Wageningen: Winand Staring Centre.

Vlek, P.L.G., Kuhne, R.F. and Denich, M. 1997 Nutrient resources for crop production in the tropics. *Phil. Trans. R. Soc. Lond.* B **352**, 975–985.

Young, A. 1998 *Land resources: now and for the future.* Cambridge University Press.

The European wood balance

Sten Nilsson

International Institute for Applied Systems Analysis (IIASA), A-2361 Laxenburg, Austria

Background

To discuss the future consumption and supply of wood in Europe I believe it would be of interest to create a European wood balance as a platform for the discussion. Several studies have been performed to illustrate future trends in consumption and supply of wood in the world (see, for example, United Nations 1996; Solberg *et al*. 1996; Food and Agriculture Organization 1997). In this case I shall use the latest available information on this issue as a platform for the discussion (Wood Resources International 1998, 1999). However, to discuss this kind of analysis there is a need to define what we mean by wood supply. One basic approach used is the 'biological supply'. In this case, the supply is defined as the sustainable yield (net annual growth or annual allowable cut) on productive, close non-reserved forests (see, for example, Wood Resources International 1998). However, to sort out a more realistic supply, the impact of government policies on, for example, forest utilization, development of utilization technologies, landowner attitudes, land-use and environmental constraints on biological wood supply have to be considered.

This measure is what can be realistically expected to happen, given the multiple policy constraints on vogue and technical constraints (Apsey & Reed 1995). This supply is called 'cut potential' (see, for example, Jaakko Pöyry 1994), 'timber availability' (Apsey & Reed 1995) or 'probable wood supply' (see, for example, Wood Resources International 1998). The probable supply is substantially lower than the biological wood supply. In the following text I use the term 'possible wood supply' for this supply. The third level of supply is the 'economic wood supply', taking market constraints into account and 'economic supply' is defined as the equilibrium solution in a supply–demand game given a number of additional economic constraints. Normally the 'economic supply' is lower than the 'possible supply' because the element of cost has been explicitly introduced and compared with prices. In some regions, significant amounts of 'possible supply' are not economically viable given the price trends and real increase in production costs for wood.

Wood balance for Europe

The wood balance (how supply matches demand) is based on analysis by Wood Resources International (1999) and has an outlook to the year 2030. Included in Europe are western Europe, eastern Europe and European Russia. The productive, closed non-reserved forests available or exploitable for industrial wood production are: western Europe 96.3 Mha, eastern Europe 37.5 Mha, and European Russia 166.2 Mha. In western and eastern Europe the area of exploitable forests has been more or less constant since the 1960s. However, during the same period there has been an increase in non-exploitable forest areas (Kuusela 1994). The area of the exploitable forests of

Million m³ Roundwood Equivalents

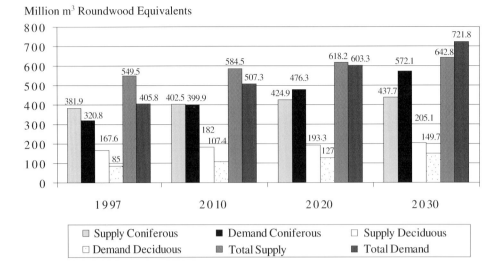

Figure 1. Outlook on the European wood balance.

European Russia has, during the same period, increased slightly (5 Mha) but the growing stock (volume) has increased by nearly 30%. In western and eastern Europe only *ca.* 1% of the forests consists of original forests or old growth but there are still substantial areas of old-growth forest in European Russia. The balance is expressed in roundwood equivalents, which means that the consumption (demand) of different forest industrial products is converted to roundwood equivalents. The supply used is 'possible supply' and the 'demand' only includes the consumption of industrial forest products. An outlook of the wood balance to the year 2030 is presented in Figure 1. Thus, the wood balance is based on the principle of self-sufficiency in Europe.

From Figure 1 it can be seen that the consumption of industrial coniferous wood is estimated to increase by some 250 million cubic metres of roundwood equivalents during the studied period in Europe. The consumption of industrial deciduous wood is estimated to increase by some 65 million cubic metres of roundwood equivalents. A summarizing wood balance is presented in Table 1.

The wood balance shows that, around the year 2020, Europe will be forced to import *ca.* 50 million cubic metres of roundwood equivalents of coniferous wood to satisfy demand. This import need will probably be supplied by import from the Southern Hemisphere. By 2030 the import need increases to about 135 million cubic metres. During the whole period there will be a satisfactory supply of deciduous wood. The total wood balance for Europe shows an approximate balance for the year 2020 but in 2030 the total 'deficit' is some 80 million cubic metres of roundwood equivalents.

There are, of course, a lot of uncertainties in calculations of this kind but they are necessary as a framework for analysing the future consumption and supply of wood in Europe.

Table 1. Outlook on the European wood balance to the year 2030

	European wood balance/10⁶ m³ roundwood equivalents			
	1997	2010	2020	2030
total	+143.7	+77.2	+14.9	− 79.0
coniferous	+ 61.1	+ 2.6	−51.4	−134.4
deciduous	+ 82.6	+74.6	+66.3	+ 55.4

Wood for energy

Only industrial wood is included in the wood balance discussed in Figure 1 and Table 1. Wood is also used for energy production. However, there are very big uncertainties in existing estimates on current fuel wood consumption (see, for example, Nilsson 1996). Very few countries have reliable and consistent statistics on wood consumption for fuel and there are uncertainties on how much of the fuel wood consumed can be classified as real wood (or how much fuel wood is coming from the 'possible supply'). However, it can be concluded that the major countries using forest biomass for energy in western Europe are the Nordic countries (*ca*. 600 PJ per year). The rest of western Europe uses *ca*. 1250 PJ in total per year with France, Spain, Turkey, Italy, Austria and Germany as the major consumers. The consumption in eastern Europe is *ca*. 200 PJ and in European Russia is estimated to be 1000 PJ. There is also the political drive to develop a 'wood for energy sector' to substitute fossil fuels. These political initiatives can drive the fuel wood consumption in different directions. I have tried to introduce the fuel wood issue in the wood balance by using a conservative estimate on future fuel wood consumption in Europe based on figures in Wood Resources International (1998) and Nilsson & Shvidenko (1999). By taking the fuel wood situation into account we get a summarized wood balance, which is presented in Table 2.

In this case the European wood balance is already negative from a self-sufficiency point of view and the region would have a total deficit of *ca*. 325 million cubic metres of roundwood equivalents in the year 2030. However, it should be underlined that the current negative balance is a theoretical measure based on self-sufficiency. In reality, Europe is today importing wood products from regions outside Europe to a value of approx. US$15 billion. It also means that the existing 'possible supply' in Europe is far from utilized today.

Sustainable supply

It is difficult to judge how much 'sustainability' there is included in the term 'possible supply', which is used as a basis for the calculations illustrated in Figure 1 and Tables 1 and 2. Some of the sustainability aspects are taken into account, such as the harvest's not exceeding growth, the exclusion of current protected areas from harvests, and the inclusion of current environmental regulations. However, the term does not reflect or take into account all aspects of the current debate on sustainable forest management.

Duinker *et al*. (1998) argue that the sustainability concept encompasses all human requirements, with the goal of increasing human welfare and aggregate benefits from the forests. This concept implies that, for example, the production of wood, the maintenance of biological diversity and the sequestration of greenhouse gases are the means and not the objectives—optimal human welfare being the overall objective.

It can be concluded that many analyses have been published on future trends in the production and consumption of wood, but there are difficulties in drawing conclusions about sustainability from the analyses. In what follows I shall illustrate a couple of issues, which are important to take into account in the sustainability analysis in sustaining forests and development in Europe.

Table 2. Outlook on the European wood balance to the year 2030, including fuel wood

	European wood balance/10^6 m^3 roundwood equivalents			
	1997	2010	2020	2030
total	− 90.3	−165.8	−231.1	−327.0
coniferous	+ 11.1	− 46.4	−100.4	−183.4
deciduous	−101.4	−119.4	−130.7	−143.6

Biodiversity
Forests contain at least two-thirds of the earth's terrestrial species. Steps should be taken, such as an increase in protected areas and reserves and a biodiversity-oriented management, to avoid the irreversible loss of biodiversity in any forest region of the world. The debate is intense concerning how large areas should be protected.

Climate change
One of the most important environmental concerns is man-induced climate change. Forests have a dual role in climate as both source and sink of greenhouse gases.

Soil and water protection
Stabilizing soil, preventing erosion, controlling water run-off in catchment areas, providing protection from wind, heat and dust are all roles for forests. The global pool of stocks of carbon in forests (vegetation, soil and below ground biomass) is estimated to be *ca.* 1146 Gt of carbon or nearly 50% of all carbon stored in the world's terrestrial ecosystems. The global deforestation is estimated to cause emissions of 1.6 Gt of carbon per year.

Amenity and well-being
There are limited statistics on requirements of forests related to the provision of amenity and well-being. Nilsson (1996) estimates that, during a 10-year period in Europe, areas with a high to medium demand for different amenity and well-being functions increased by 10–30%.

These are just some of the sustainability issues to take into account in the future wood balance for Europe. (For a more detailed discussion on forestry for sustainable development and sustainable forest management, see Duinker *et al.* (1998).)

Translating ecological sustainability into criteria for forest management means something like the following:

- protection of biodiversity (genetic, species, ecological and landscape);
- provision of high ecosystem productivity;
- soil conservation;
- water management;
- protection of ecosystem functioning and process;
- contribution to carbon sequestration and other global ecological services.

However, the concept of sustainability includes not only ecological sustainability but also social and economic sustainability, with social sustainability becoming increasingly important. Social sustainability means 'the capacity for future generations to maintain cultural patterns of life and adapt to evolving societal and ecological conditions'. It also means forest management criteria, which include the following:

- sustainable supply of social benefits;
- long-term output of multiple economic benefits;
- protection of the amenity;
- recognition of indigenous rights and knowledge of historical and archaeological sites.

What does it mean for our outlook on the European wood balance if Europe is going to live up to all of these requirements? We do not know. We can get an indication of the direction from analyses performed in Sweden on the impact of the Swedish regulation of excluding 5% of the forest area from active forestry, an additional 5% of forest area to comply with the requirements of the Forest Stewardship Council (FSC) for certification (i.e. that timber has come from well-managed forests)

Table 3. *Outlook on the European wood balance to the year 2030, including fuel wood and some of the sustainability concerns*

| | European wood balance/10^6 m^3 roundwood equivalents | | | |
	1997	2010	2020	2030
total	−172.7	−253.1	−323.8	−423.4
coniferous	− 46.2	−106.4	−164.1	−249.0
deciduous	−126.5	−146.7	−159.7	−174.4

and the application of other rules required by the FSC for certification in Sweden. Swedish analyses have tried to quantify the long-term impact on wood supply and found that the supply would be reduced by *ca*. 15%. This is only covering a part of the ecological criteria discussed above, but if we apply this conservative number to our European case we get a result shown in Table 3.

Even only taking into account the sustainability issues defined above for certification will worsen the European self-sufficiency balance substantially. The total 'deficit' will already increase by some 100 million cubic metres of roundwood equivalents from the year 2010. This indicates that taking into account all aspects of ecological and social sustainability will have a marked impact on the wood supply and wood balances of Europe. However, as discussed above, to enhance human well-being through the sustainable management of Europe's forests also includes a strong economic component. Without economic development in forestry there will probably be a reduced enhancement of human well-being from forestry.

There is a trade-off between economic sustainability and ecological and, to some extent, social (socio-economic) sustainability. Nilsson (1996) has discussed the economic impact of the rules implemented for certification (discussed above for the calculation presented in Table 3) on the basis of case studies performed in Canada, Finland and Sweden and finds that there will be a decrease in the economic results (profits) in forestry of 15–25% by just implementing the certification rules. Additional considerations of sustainability are bound to decrease the economic result further. This makes the situation complicated in the future for the European forest sector. The internationalization of the forest sector is currently proceeding rapidly. This development causes a sharp competition between the producers. New investments are taking place in low-cost regions (cheap wood) and close to the markets where there is rapid growth, such as South-East Asia, Latin America and the southern states of the USA. The current European economic competitive position is illustrated in Figure 2 in the form of delivered wood costs to the industry (which is one of the major cost components of the forest industry). Figure 2 illustrates coniferous wood but the picture is similar for deciduous wood. Thus, the additional costs for meeting the requirements on sustainability will decrease even further the competitive position for the European forest sector. This means that Europe would have to be supplied with forest products from other regions outside Europe to a larger extent than today.

Lessons from wood balances

It is obvious that the consumption of forest products will continue to increase in Europe. If we look at the wood balances for Europe based on self-sufficiency, the total theoretical 'deficit' would be *ca*. 80 million cubic metres of roundwood equivalents in 30 years if the industrial wood were taken into account. In adding the very uncertain estimates of wood for energy consumption the 'deficit' might increase to *ca*. 325 million cubic metres. Europe is moving towards forestry for sustainability and sustainable forest management. However, the implementation of the certification of forests alone will probably increase the deficit in the wood balance to *ca*. 425 million cubic metres. If all aspects of sustainability are implemented, the deficit will be even greater. It is obvious that there

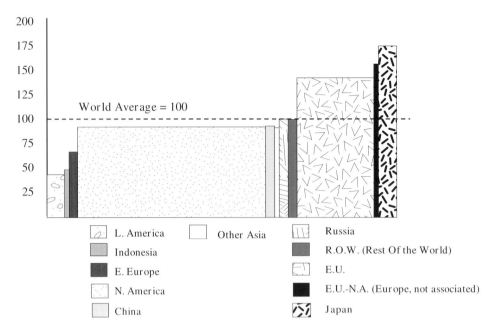

Figure 2. *Relative delivered coniferous wood costs in the world.*

are trade-offs between economic, ecological and social sustainability in the European forest sector. This is illustrated by Figure 3. It can also be expressed that individual parcels of land can be managed either as long-lasting tree farms for industry or as long-lasting wilderness preserves, but not both at once.

What are the options for Europe in the future?

Increased importation

We have studied a simplified model of a self-sufficient Europe using all of its 'possible supply'. In reality, all of Europe's 'possible supply' is not used and we are today importing substantial amounts of forest products from outside Europe, with a value of US$15 billion in 1996. Thus, an increased consumption and reduced supply by intensified concerns about sustainability can be taken care of by increased importation. However, this might not be good for the rest of the world. Sohngen *et al.* (1999) have investigated the global impact of increased forest conservation efforts in North America and Europe. They conclude that if 5% and 10% of the productive forest land are set aside in North America and Europe respectively for conservation, 1.5 and 2 Mha per year respectively of currently economically inaccessible forests will be harvested somewhere else. The authors state 'these additional harvests will likely occur in tropical areas'. The set-asides will increase the world market prices of wood by 1–2%, making it economically feasible to harvest forests from areas in which it was previously too expensive.

In the worst case this might mean that Europe would be exporting the sustainability problem to other regions of the world.

Tree plantations in the Southern Hemisphere

Several authors have argued that one way in which to save natural forests would be to increase the area of plantations in the Southern Hemisphere. This means that Europe should contribute to establishing plantations primarily on degraded agricultural land in the tropics. Nilsson &

Relative Ecological and Social Sustainability

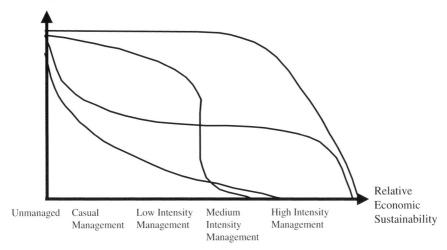

Figure 3. Principles for interaction between ecological sustainability, social sustainability, economic sustainability and forest management. (Data manipulated from Mooney et al. (1996).)

Schopfhauser (1995) have estimated what a large-scale afforestation programme could contribute to the global carbon balance. It is assumed that 345 Mha globally could be available for plantations and agroforestry, which could increase the carbon fixation in forests by 1.5 Gt per year but only about 60 years after the plantation programme was implemented.

Differentiated land use and forest management in Europe
On the basis of the discussion above, it can be concluded that a plausible way in the future for Europe to avoid sustainability conflicts and improve the wood balance would be to identify areas invaluable for environmental and social sustainability and devote and manage them as nature and social preserves. However, Europe would also need to identify areas that can be used for timber production through different intensity in forest management (soft, normal and intensive forest management; see Figure 3). This is in line with North American conclusions and is in fact how Russian forestry is organized.

Case studies in Sweden show that this differentiated land use and forest management is fully implementable. The case studies performed show that the differentiated approach can result in even higher production than traditional forestry (multi-purpose) in Europe. However, the costs are somewhat higher but these can probably be borne because of the future increased timber prices projected by Sohngen *et al.* (1999).

Uncertain future
This paper has used a simplified approach in trying to illustrate the impact of increased consumption and concerns about sustainability on the future European wood balance. A major issue for discussion here has been the future European wood supply but it is important to point out that the European forests are not a just a fibre source but an ecological/social/economic spider web of interrelationships.

The world might also see the development of information technology, engineered wood and replacement of wood products, which would change the future European consumption of forest products.

References

Apsey, M. & Reed, L. 1995 *World timber resources outlook, current perceptions. A discussion paper*. Vancouver: Council of Forest Industries.

Duinker, P.N., Nilsson, S. & Chipeta, M.E. 1998 Forestry for sustainable development and global fiber supply. *Unasylva* **49**, no. 193.

Food and Agriculture Organization 1997 *FAO provisional outlook for global forest products consumption, production and trade to 2010*. Rome: Food and Agriculture Organization of the United Nations.

Jaakko Pöyry 1994 *Fast-growing plantations: increasing role in wood trade and securing wood supply*. Helsinki: Jaakko Pöyry Oy.

Kuusela, K. 1994 *Forest resources in Europe*. Cambridge University Press.

Mooney, H.A., Cushman, J.H., Medina, E., Suta, O.E. & Schulz, E.-D. (eds) 1996 *Functional roles of biodiversity: a global perspective*. Chichester: Wiley.

Nilsson, S. 1996 *Do we have enough forests*? Vienna: International Union of Forestry Research Organizations.

Nilsson, S. & Schopfhauser, W. 1995 The carbon-sequestration potential of a global afforestation program. *Climatic Change* **30**, 267–293.

Nilsson, S. & Shvidenko, A. 1999 *The Ukrainian forest sector in a global perspective*. Interim Report IR-99-011. Laxenburg, Austria: International Institute for Applied Systems Analysis.

Sohngen, B., Mendelsohn, R. & Sedjo, R. 1999 Forest management conservation and global markets. *American Journal of Agricultural Economics* **81** (1), 1–13.

Solberg, B., Brooks, D., Pajuoja, H., Peck, T.J. & Wardle, P.A. 1996 *Long-term trends and prospects in world supply and demand for wood and implications for sustainable forest management*. Research Report no. 6. Joensuu, Finland: European Forest Institute.

United Nations 1996 *European forest and timber: scenarios for the 21st century*. New York and Geneva: United Nations.

Wood Resources International 1998 *Global wood fiber study. Final report to European Commission*. Reston, Virginia: Wood Resources International Ltd.

Wood Resources International 1999 *The global timber supply/demand balance to 2030: has the equation changed?* Reston, Virginia: Wood Resources International Ltd.

Sustainable consumption and fisheries

Demetres Karavellas

World Wide Fund for Nature (WWF) Greece, Filellinon 26, Athens 10558, Greece

Introduction

Fish are, among other things, important sources of food and income. On a global scale, 19% of animal protein for human consumption is derived from fish, in a fisheries sector that employs close to 200 million people. Between 35% and 40% of fisheries production is traded annually, rendering fish a truly international foodstuff.

Whereas the world's fishing fleet has grown significantly faster than its catches, fuelled in part by growing demand, the critical situation of world fisheries is making it increasingly apparent that fundamental reform of fisheries management is essential for the long-term health of the marine ecosystems and the millions of people who depend on them.

The present paper seeks to address the sustainability challenge as it applies to fisheries. This is followed by a brief examination of the present status of world fisheries and their degree of relation to sustainable development. Finally, the paper arrives at a series of proposed actions deemed essential to place fisheries on the road to sustainability.

Sustainable consumption and fisheries

The concept of sustainable consumption is inevitably linked to that of sustainable development. The latter was the central theme of discussion at the UN Conference on Environment and Development in Rio, in 1992. Over the years, a variety of definitions for this concept have been developed. The World Commission on Environment and Development in 1987 adopted the following simple definition: 'Development that meets the need of the present without compromising the ability of future generations to meet their own needs'.

At the 94th meeting of the FAO Committee on Fisheries, this definition was elaborated as follows (Food and Agriculture Organization 1991):

> Sustainable development is the management and conservation of the natural resource base, and the orientation of technological and institutional change in such a manner as to ensure the attainment and continued satisfaction of human needs for present and future generations. Such development conserves land, water, plant and genetic resources, is environmentally non-degrading, technologically appropriate, economically viable and socially acceptable.

IUCN (The World Conservation Union), the United Nations Environment Programme (UNEP) and the World Wide Fund for Nature (WWF), in developing their 'Strategy for Sustainable Living' (IUCN/UNEP/WWF 1991), based the strategy on three fundamental points:

The first is simple and obvious. It is that we, the world's people, want to survive; but more than that, we want a satisfactory life for all of us and for our descendants. To achieve that goal, we need a new kind of development and we must learn to live differently.

The second is that we depend on the resources of the Earth to meet our basic and vital needs; if they are diminished or deteriorate, we risk that our needs and those of our descendants will go unmet. Because we have been failing to care for the Earth properly and living unsustainably, that risk has become dangerously high. We are now gambling with the survival of civilisation.

The third point is that we need not lose. We can eliminate the risk by ensuring that the benefits of development are distributed equitably, and by learning to care for the Earth and live sustainably.

This same strategy uses the term 'sustainable development' to mean 'improving the quality of human life while living within the carrying capacity of human ecosystems'.

The Marine Stewardship Council, an independent non-governmental initiative aimed at engaging market forces to promote sustainable fisheries, has produced a series of principles and criteria that reflect the recognition that a sustainable fishery should be based on the following components:

- the maintenance of the integrity of ecosystems;
- the maintenance and re-establishment of healthy populations of targeted species;
- the development and maintenance of effective fisheries management systems, taking into account all relevant biological, technological, economic, social, environmental and commercial aspects; and
- compliance with relevant international, national and local laws and standards.

Irrespective of the exact terminology chosen to reflect the conceptual framework accurately, does the present status of fisheries and their management worldwide approximate conditions of sustainable development? If not, what can be proposed to rectify this situation? As a first step, it is considered useful that the present status of global fisheries be reviewed in brief.

The present status of global fisheries

Capture fisheries are clearly facing their limits. The Food and Agriculture Organization (1996a) reports that 70% of the world's commercially important marine fish stocks are either fully fished, overexploited, depleted or slowly recovering. The same organization has recorded 16 major fishery species whose global catch has declined by more than 50% over the past 30 years (Weber 1994). The dire situation of the more commercially important species such as bluefin tuna, haddock and Atlantic cod led the IUCN to add these to its 'Red List' of endangered species.

With the more traditionally valuable species being fished out to the level of commercial extinction, attention is increasingly being shifted to the species farther down in the food chain such as sardine, pilchard and anchovy, which are also used for the production of fish meal and fish oils. Such 'fishing down' of the food chain has occurred in the North Sea, where the Norway pout has replaced the cod as a valued species.

The lack of ownership of resources, in combination with unrestricted access to the industry, has contributed to an economic overcapitalization so great that the fishing industry on a global scale has been calculated as operating with a net loss of approx. US$54 billion (Food and Agriculture Organization 1996; see also Millazzo 1998; Steenblik & Munro 1999). Inevitably, these costs are met through government grants and subsidies. In the medium and long term, such subsidies might in fact contribute to overcapacity by attempting to bolster the profitability of fishing, stimulating investment that might not otherwise occur and deterring the departure of fishers from overcapitalized fisheries (World Wide Fund for Nature 1997). An analysis of data from the 14 leading fishing countries has indicated a level of *ca*. 150% in global fleet over-capacity. The FAO has calculated that by subsidizing overfishing, governments are wasting, on an annual basis, three to seven times the amount of capital required to rectify the situation (House of Lords Select Committee on Science and Technology 1996). More recent estimates indicate that the size of the world's fishing fleet would have to decrease by at least 25% for revenues to match operating costs (Garcia & Newton 1997).

While the trends of over-fishing become increasingly prevalent and painfully visible at all levels, evidence is also mounting that fisheries have a significant effect on marine biodiversity and are characterized by a high degree of wastage of resources from the discarding of unwanted catches at sea. It has been estimated that discarding amounts to an average of 27 Mt per year, representing almost one-third of the total reported annual production of marine capture fisheries (Food and Agriculture Organization 1996). The problem of by-catch and discarding is a serious one and has been a cause of major concern over the past few years. Although possible solutions are by no means simple or straightforward, they are to the benefit of all, including the fishers who incur additional costs, associated with sorting and dumping, yet generate no additional revenue.

Finally, the destruction and degradation of the marine environment from anthropogenic activities related to and independent of fisheries must be taken into consideration. Coastal ecosystems in particular are being placed under considerable strain from a variety of sources and user groups who, although sharing their 'dependence' on the coastal zone, usually operate as dispersed and independent units, paying little attention to the impact of their practices on other users of the natural resources (Organization for Economic Co-operation and Development 1996).

Without a doubt, the present state of global fisheries cannot be described to resemble conditions of sustainable development. Growth, rather than sustainability, seems to be the term that more appropriately describes the fisheries policy of governments throughout the world. The inclination of markets towards short-term profits have rendered long-term sustainability of catches a difficult if almost impossible management goal. The gap between intention and actions in creating sustainable fisheries is far from being closed.

Future projections indicate a widening gap between the world's demand for fish and the ability of the oceans to meet it (Masood 1997). It has been estimated that fish required for human consumption will reach 110–120 Mt by 2010, in comparison with the 82 Mt caught in 1995 (World Resources Institute 1999). The same source predicts that demand for non-food fish products will be between 30 and 33 Mt. Overall, therefore, the total demand for both fish types might reach 153 Mt, an increase of up to 35% on 1995 catch levels.

FAO analyses have indicated that marine capture fisheries, under the present *modus operandi*, could not sustain more than 90 Mt. This number could perhaps be increased by 15 Mt with substantial improvements in management regimes. The resulting gap still existing between future demand and supply is speculated, by the more optimistic, to be covered through increased aquaculture production.

The path to sustainability in fisheries: what is needed?

It must be actively acknowledged that improvements to fisheries management imply a great deal more than a slight change of status; fundamental conceptual and organizational change is needed (Stephenson & Lane 1995). Developing a new model of fisheries management is by no means a simple or straightforward task. However, the present state of world fisheries makes the need for change imperative. Although such change does imply sacrifice and might carry a political cost in the short and medium terms, effective management will accrue considerable benefits in the future. The FAO has calculated that, within a decade, 'the difference between the gains which might be achieved through efficient management and the losses which will come from the pursuit of present practices, could be of the order of 20 million tonnes of fish landed per year' (Food and Agriculture Organization 1997).

The World Wide Fund for Nature (WWF) has recently proposed a series of actions that are considered essential in accelerating the transition towards sustainable, well-managed fisheries (Kemf *et al.* 1996). These are presented below.

Strengthening of national, regional and international capacity to manage marine fisheries

Sufficient funds must be allocated to developing the scientific and technical capabilities needed for effective management. International bodies and governments charged with the task of managing fisheries must demonstrate political boldness and strive to translate the spirit and content of recent international initiatives (UN Agreement on Straddling Fish Stocks & Highly Migratory Fish Stocks; FAO Code of Conduct for Responsible Fisheries) into action. Among other things, these new initiatives reflect a precautionary approach that fosters a transition to more sustainable fisheries. Moreover, they open decision-making procedures to public scrutiny and stakeholder participation, an important prerequisite to fundamental change.

Focus of management programmes on limiting effort and restricting access to fisheries

Management schemes must be developed that effectively limit fishing effort, particularly in over-fished or depleted fisheries. Limited-access programmes should prevent new entry into fisheries that are fully subscribed and form a part of comprehensive management plans for each fishery.

Adoption and implementation of recovery plans for depleted species

Depleted species, such as the Northern Atlantic Bluefin Tuna (*Thunnus thynnus*) are not subject to any form of a comprehensive recovery plan. Priority should be placed on developing and implementing effective recovery plans, which should incorporate target population sizes and timetables for their achievement. These plans should ultimately be driven by the biological requirements of the fish populations, not the short-term demands of the fishing industry.

Reduction and elimination of destructive fishery subsidies

The vast amounts of capital that are used to prop up unsustainable fisheries should be eliminated without delay. At a recent workshop organized by WWF and UNEP in Geneva, and attended by a large range of intergovernmental and non-governmental organizations, a clear link was established between the tens of millions of dollars of subsidies paid to the fishing sector annually, the resulting overcapacity in the industry and the problem of global fisheries depletion. Where subsidies are provided, they should be part of a comprehensive plan with resource sustainability being the primary objective. Shifting the concept of management systems to address the economic causes, rather than the symptoms, of overexploitation is an important condition for change.

Expansion of retraining programmes for fishers displaced by overfishing and effort limitation

Retraining programmes are urgently required for transferring displaced fishers into other sectors of productive employment and to avoid social unrest. Funds for such programmes should be secured as a priority and allocated in combination with decommissioning programmes.

Reduction of the 'footprint' of developed countries on Third World fisheries

Throughout the world, northern states are investing huge sums in gaining access to the fishing grounds of developing countries and often result in the transfer of overcapacity to another area. In the European Union (EU), a draft report of the European Parliament on International Fisheries Agreements (European Parliament 1997) aptly states that the 'over-capacity of the EU cannot be exported indefinitely'. New standards should be developed that will reduce the impact of northern fleets. Fisheries agreements should be negotiated on the basis of ensuring, at a minimum, the long-term sustainability of resources, local communities and the fisheries sector as a whole. A full assessment of the impacts of fishing activities on the specific fisheries, their associated marine ecosystems and local fishing communities should precede the signing of any agreement in the future.

Reduction and elimination of by-catch

Although no single or simple solution can be offered for this problem, a great deal can be said for the development of various technological approaches to by-catch reduction (Coonamessett Farm 1997), supported by appropriate management actions (for example closed areas). At the heart of this issue is the active acknowledgement and adoption of an ecosystem approach to fisheries management that addresses the effects of fishing in a more holistic manner, not confining analyses solely to impacts on target species.

Development of social and economic incentives for sustainable fisheries

Market forces themselves can be used to create the incentives for sustainable fisheries. Ultimately, when conservation and economic goals can be made to coincide, the sustainable use of resources will become a more feasible goal (Sutton 2000). On a practical basis, this also implies the need for active collaboration between representatives from the conservation community on the one hand, and the fishing industry on the other. In early 1996, WWF formed such a partnership with Unilever Corporation, with the aim of creating economic incentives for sustainable fisheries through the establishment of the Marine Stewardship Council (MSC). As an independent, non-profit, non-governmental body, the MSC will establish, through an extensive consultative process, a broad set of principles for sustainable fisheries and will set standards for individual fisheries. Only fisheries meeting these standards will be eligible for certification by independent, accredited certifying firms. Ultimately, products from MSC-certified fisheries will be marked with an on-pack logo, allowing consumers to select products that originate from a sustainable source. As this is a voluntary scheme ultimately dependent on stakeholder participation and endorsement, it is hoped that this innovative market approach will contribute towards the goal of sustainable fisheries.

Conclusion

No one of the above proposals on its own is sufficient to alter the status of global fisheries towards sustainability, nor is this list considered to be an exhaustive one. Collectively, however, and in combination with the realization by all stakeholders that conceptual change is long overdue, there is still the chance for crafting a different future.

References

Coonamessett Farm 1997 *A review of technological approaches to bycatch reduction*. Report prepared for the World Wide Fund for Nature UK. Godalming, UK: World Wildlife Fund.

European Parliament 1997 *Draft report on international fisheries agreements*. Committee on Fisheries, February 1997. PE 220.881. Brussels: European Parliament.

Food and Agriculture Organization 1991 *Environment and sustainability in fisheries*. COFI Document COFI/91/3, December 1990. FO: RAS/85/017. Rome: Food and Agriculture Organization.

Food and Agriculture Organization 1996 *The state of world fisheries and aquaculture*. Rome: Food and Agriculture Organization.

Food and Agriculture Organization 1997 *Major issues in world fisheries*. COFI Document COFI/97/2, March 1997. Rome: Food and Agriculture Organization.

Garcia, S.M. & Newton, C. 1997 Current situation, trends and prospects in world capture fisheries. In *Global trends: fisheries management* (American Fisheries Symposium no. 20) (eds E.K. Pikitch, D.D. Huppert & M.P. Sissenswine), pp. 3–27. Bethesda, Maryland: American Fisheries Society.

House of Lords Select Committee on Science and Technology 1996 *Fish stock conservation and management*. Session 1995–96, 2nd Report. London: House of Lords Select Committee on Science and Technology.

IUCN/UNEP/WWF 1991 *Caring for the Earth. A strategy for sustainable living*. Gland, Switzerland: IUCN and WWF; Nairobi: United Nations Environment Programme.

Kemf, E., Sutton, M. & Wilson, A. 1996 *Marine fishes in the wild*. Godalming, UK: World Wide Fund for Nature.

Masood, E. 1997 Fisheries science: all at sea when it comes to politics? *Nature* **386**, 105–106.

Millazzo, M. 1998 *Subsidies in world fisheries: a re-examination*. Washington, DC: World Bank.

Organization for Economic Co-operation and Development 1996 *Reconciling pressures on the coastal zone: fisheries and aquaculture*. Paris: Organization for Economic Co-operation and Development.

Steenblik, R.P. & Munro, G.R. 1999 International work on fishing subsidies: an update. In *Overcapacity, over-capitalisation and subsidies in European fisheries* (eds A. Hatcher & K. Robinson), pp. 254–269. Portsmouth: Center for Economics and Management of Aquatic Resources, University of Portsmouth.

Stephenson, R.L. & Lane, D.E. 1995 Fisheries management science: a plea for conceptual change. *Canadian Journal of Fisheries and Aquatic Science* **52**, 2051–2056.

Sutton, M. (2000) Reversing the crisis in marine fisheries: the role of non-governmental organisations. In *Proceedings of the 30th Annual Conference of the Law of the Sea Institute, Al-Ain, United Arab Emirates, 19–22 May 1996*. (In preparation.)

Weber, P. 1994 *Net loss: fish, jobs, and the marine environment*. Washington, DC: Worldwatch Institute.

World Commission on Environment and Development 1987 *Our common future*. Oxford University Press.

World Resources Institute 1999 *Critical consumption trends and implications: degrading Earth's Ecosystems*. Washington, DC: World Resources Institute.

World Wide Fund for Nature 1997 *Subsidies and depletion of world fisheries: case studies*. Godalming, UK: World Wide Fund for Nature.

A European perspective on sustainable consumption of freshwater: Is getting rid of pollutants realistic and affordable?

Malin Falkenmark

Natural Science Research Council, and Stockholm International Water Institute, SE-106 36 Stockholm, Sweden

The gap between politicians and scientists is worth contemplating further. Politicians tend to sign to well formulated principles which are not always followed. They can therefore be perceived as doubtful with regard to the likelihood of adhering to them. … This raises the question whether politicians are really well informed, but also emphasises the duty of scientists to provide adequate data and explanations. In other words, there is a choice to be made between being politically correct and being honest.

(FRN 1998)

The goal: non-undermining of the resource base

In the preparations for the Tokyo Conference on the Transition to Sustainability, consumption is 'defined as the human transformation of solid materials, liquids and energy.' Consumption is said to be of concern 'when the transformed materials, liquids and energy become less available for future use or negatively impact biophysical systems in such a way as to threaten human health, welfare and things people value' (See appendix A).

In other words, sustainable human activities are those that do not undermine their own resource base. This paper addresses the sustainability issue from a freshwater perspective, i.e. focusing on those human activities that tend to undermine the water resource base for future generations.

Water is a fundamental component of life. Humans need a continuous supply of water to keep the body functions active. The food that we eat is produced from water merging with carbon dioxide. At least 200 times more water is needed to produce the food for one person than the water needed to sustain the body functions of that person. Moreover, most activities in society depend more or less on water; so does protection from diseases, industrial production, cooling, etc.

49

Summarizing the state of understanding

Water is a unique solvent, which functions as the bloodstream of the biosphere. It carries pollutants around, it constitutes habitats for aquatic biota, and it operates plant production. Pollutants can be introduced into the mobile water in two main ways: directly through the introduction of waste products and other anthropogenic polluting substances, and indirectly from altering the dissolution capacity, for example, through acidification and through changes in the water table. Water quality genesis (Falkenmark & Allard 1989) is understood in principle for the most widespread pollutants.

Water flows underground in what can be thought of as 'stream tubes' from recharge areas higher up in the landscape to discharge/seepage areas in local hollows and valley bottoms (Figure 1). Chemical processes along these stream tubes are characterized by dissolution and absorption processes. Pollutants can accumulate in soils and sediments for later release when geochemical conditions change for some reason. Chemical bombs constitute a real risk for unexpected water pollution, and are understood only in their generalities.

Many factors complicate this simple basic pattern: interaction between chemical substances, altering geochemical conditions related to, for example, change in land use, climate change and altering water tables; geological irregularities disturbing the stream tube flow pattern (for example in karstic terrain); and time delays. The invisibility of groundwater in combination with these complexities gives a degree of 'chance' to the detection possibilities, often manifested only when a well penetrates the polluted stream tube. Although efforts at modelling the most frequent pollutants have been quite successful, the overall prediction possibilities for a certain type of pollution are full of difficulties.

Pollutants are added during water use

Water is basically used in three main ways:

- throughflow-based use of water in households and industry, where most of the water input is returned again but generally carries a certain pollution load—for households this is urine, faeces, and waste products from activities such as cleaning and washing; for industry this is liquid waste products;

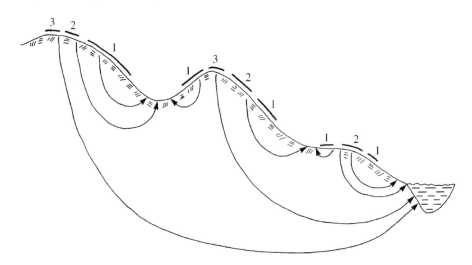

Figure 1. Main types of groundwater pathways moving along 'stream tubes' with different transit times. (From Falkenmark & Allard (1989).)

- consumptive water use for irrigation of crops, where the water involved in the biomass production processes evapotranspires to the atmosphere, that is, it is literally consumed;
- water use *in situ* in rivers or lakes for fishery, recreation, navigation, hydropower production and other uses.

Water for household and industrial use is of the most relevance from a European perspective through the pollution that it produces. During use, water gets 'enriched' with waste products and is returned to the landscape as wastewater. For a society to avoid undermining its own life support system, the water should be returned after use without a damaging pollution load. **Wastewater treatment is therefore a fundamental component of a sustainable society.**

Water for crop irrigation influences sustainability in the sense that water is literally consumed, leaving less for those living downstream (river depletion). This could be a perspective of relevance in southern and southeastern Europe, where irrigation is widespread. With such consumptive water use, sustainability would principally mean a situation in which water is allocated so that enough water remains in the river for the support of all downstream activities and for the protection of key services by the aquatic ecosystems. Because this problem will most probably be better analysed from world regions in which irrigation is the dominant water use, this paper will concentrate on the societal output of pollutants and the way in which that process reduces the usability of the water available in groundwater aquifers and rivers.

Water: a reflection of land use
Pollution loads are also added when the water moves through the landscape (above and below the ground surface) and picks up water-soluble pollutants, agricultural chemicals, pollutants from dry waste deposits and polluted soils. Some examples illustrate the scale of water pollution and its links to land use.

- **Chemical waste sites:** the combined result of underground water pathways and chemical activity is manifested in groundwater contamination under dry waste disposals (Figure 2). Buried chemical waste on waste dumps, factory sites and remote hollows has been a hot issue since the 1980s. Some 27 000 sites have been reported from Denmark (Korkman 1996). The tentative list of contaminant sites in western Europe in the 1995 Dobris assessment included more than 55 000 sites, of which 22 000 are in 'critical conditions' (European Environment Agency 1995). These figures do not include central and eastern Europe, where conditions are probably at least partly as bad. Groundwater pollution by chlorinated hydrocarbons is caused mainly by old landfills, contaminated industrial sites and industrial activities. In eastern Europe mineral oils cause heavy problems (FRN 1998).
- **Overexploitation of groundwater** is well known in many parts of Europe, where around 60% of industrial and urban centres are overexploiting their aquifers. It causes changes in the water table that can alter the hydrochemical situation in the soil from an oxygen-free to an oxygen-rich status. In Denmark, the oxidation of pyrites around city areas has caused a rise in the sulphate content of the groundwater. Nickel, and probably also arsenic, has been mobilized by the water. The former has already become a real threat to some of the Danish waterworks.
- **Agriculture:** significant increases have been observed in stream nitrate load in many water systems in Europe over the past 30–40 years in response to the large increases in fertilizer application to improve crop yields. This increase is manifested as a widespread eutrophication of lakes and coastal waters and a high nitrate content in groundwater.

Agricultural activities covering 226 Mha in Europe generate a real threat in terms of pollution with nitrate and pesticides. Large parts of Europe are already affected by nitrate levels beyond the health limit. In addition, pesticides are starting to appear in groundwater. In Denmark, pesticides have been found all over the country down to 80 m depth, mostly in groundwater recharged 10–40 years ago. Even degradation products have been identified as a greater problem in view of their persistence and mobility.

- **Mining** often results in the dewatering of aquifers and marked changes in groundwater quality. Surface water is also being contaminated by the discharge of drainage water into streams and lakes.

Chemical time bombs

Pollutants can also accumulate in soils and sediments through chemical adsorption processes in the ground that build up chemical 'time bombs' for later release when geochemical conditions change for some reason (Hekstra 1995). This means that, regardless of the speed of reducing emissions at the source, there will remain a huge legacy of old pollutants stored in soils and sediments. Although buried, they are not put away for eternity but can be remobilized.

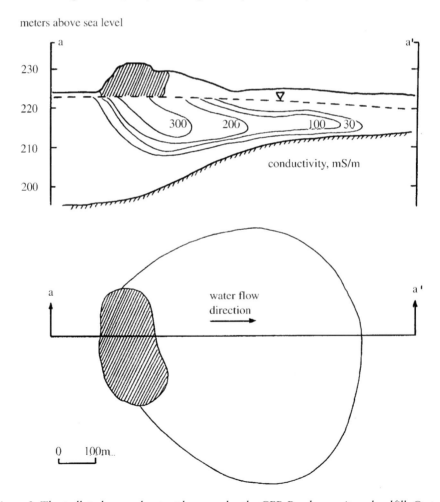

Figure 2. The polluted groundwater plume under the CFB Borden sanitary landfill, Ontario, Canada. (From Falkenmark & Allard (1989).)

Chemicals of concern are heavy metals, halogenated organics, aliphatic and aromatic hydrocarbons and synthetic fertilizers (nitrogen and phosphorus). Although lead is an example of a contaminant that has been accumulating since the Bronze Age, persistent chemicals cause the greatest concern. The retention time in soils can vary from one year to a million years. Pollutants can be released from a hidden form when water pathways and/or its chemical composition change. Such release can be triggered by changes in land use and climate that influence the controlling properties, and alter the geochemical conditions in such a way that the contaminants can be leached away by moving water.

Many possible pathways to humans

Deterioration of water quality arises from three main sectors: agriculture, industry and households. Threats to human health and well-being are due to nitrate in drinking water, pathogens associated with organic matter, and pesticides and other harmful substances. Health risks to humans can be related to many sources of contact: drinking water, polluted food (grain, fish, meat) and bathing. There is therefore a rich variety of ways by which pollutants reach the water in the landscape.

Two key processes are common to this variety: water as a **leaching agent** and water as a **transport agent**.

The water circulating through the landscape as part of the global water cycle has a number of parallel functions that contribute to the ways in which pollutants reach humans.

- The **carrier function**: water is a unique solvent continuously mobile above and below the ground, leaching the landscape and its soil and rock layers. The burden is carried back to the ground surface unless it degrades or is absorbed along the water pathways.
- The **health function**: humans and all living creatures are absolutely dependent on daily access to water for survival. Water is also fundamental for hygiene purposes in washing away infectious matter. In these ways polluted water reaches the water systems. At the same time, water becomes polluted by sanitary and other human waste.
- The **socio-economic production function**: water is a major 'lubricant' in economic activities, especially industry. This process involves contact between the water used and the pollutants involved in the processes.
- The **habitat function**: by this function, biota in aquatic ecosystems become polluted and might later be eaten by humans. This makes polluted fish a threat to human health (as with mercury-polluted lakes).
- The **biomass production in agriculture** operated by water taken in through the roots and intensified by irrigation: this process can involve the transfer of pollutants from the soil or from irrigation water to the plant, which might later be eaten by humans.

Groundwater pollution: invisible, irreversible and difficult to detect

Two-thirds of people in Europe rely on groundwater for their water needs (European Environment Agency 1996). This makes groundwater pollution particularly serious and a large hidden problem of sustainability for the future in Europe. The existence of pollution in groundwater does not mean that it is readily detected by society. Pollution can remain hidden owing to long transit times.

Moreover, groundwater pollution has generally to be seen as more or less irreversible in the lifetime of a human being. The reason is that an aquifer cannot be freed from pollutants any more quickly than the time needed for fresh, unpolluted water to pass through it and replace the polluted water.

Within the given definition of sustainability, water contamination by the leaching of pollutants from land use must be seen as a major threat to sustainable consumption of fresh water. Transition to sustainability therefore means learning to control the leaching of pollutants from land use.

Will the transition to sustainability be affordable?

The problem of contaminated soils and the risk that they constitute for groundwater pollution is spectacular. Korkman (1996) reports, for example, that the task of investigating and carrying through remedial activities in Denmark is more than can be accomplished in 20–30 years and will exceed the resources that the country can afford without disturbing the economy. The cost estimated for the European Union (EU) is more than 100 billion Ecu.

As regards the fertilizer problem, the European Environment Agency has estimated from model computations that nitrate has polluted groundwater beyond potability limits beneath more than 85% of agricultural land in western, central and eastern Europe. In France the groundwater has nitrate levels beyond the health limit over some 40% of the area. A French newspaper, *Le Journal de Dimanche*, reported in 1996 that in 10–12 years 70% of the water sources in the province of Bretagne will be unusable. Interestingly enough, farmers are unwilling to change their habits and even refuse to accept that certain municipalities are declared vulnerable.

Costs for decreasing pollution by nitrate are difficult to assess. Best agricultural practices are not enough to decrease nitrate as required. An additional problem reported from Denmark is that soil is seen as property that goes with the land. Steps taken towards its protection therefore depend on voluntary agreements. Danish farmers even claim, through their farmer associations, that they should have compensation for not polluting the groundwater. In Stuttgart, according to Kobus (1996), the city inhabitants have to contribute, through their water tariffs, to compensate farmers for reducing their fertilizer use to protect the aquifer from which the city gets its water.

The European Environment Agency (1995) also reported that the threat from pesticidal groundwater pollution is especially large under coarse textured soils in Denmark, northern France, The Netherlands, Lithuania and Belarus. Korkman (1996) is more pessimistic, noting that the problem might be much more extensive because in Denmark pesticides are also found in aquifers under clay materials. The cost of remediation of the damage caused by the use of pesticides is almost impossible to calculate.

Generations of pollution abatement strategies

Water quality management can be oriented reactively or proactively. The former involves the control of human exposure wherever pollution is already widespread. Protection of the quality of drinking water (especially from harmful organisms and chemicals) is a prerequisite for good health. Key measures are monitoring, quality control and purification of drinking water.

Proactive water quality management, in contrast, involves minimizing the flow of harmful substances from land to water. It is an issue of sanitation, of minimizing industrial waste production, and of more environmentally sound strategies for the handling and use of agricultural chemicals. The successful implementation of such measures depends on strong legislation and enforcement, well-coordinated administrative units, awareness of the problem in the business sectors, and overcoming fundamental difficulties of controlling land use by land owners and users.

Societal reactions to disturbances in water quality may evolve a number of strategic decisions (Falkenmark & Allard 1989):

1. No problem: amounts are too small to detect consequences;
2. Some problem: dilute the pollutant to bring concentrations down to semi-natural levels;
3. Evident problem: isolate the pollution source by use of various barriers, for example by raw water purification to prevent human consumption of polluted water;
4. Large problem: avoid escape of the pollutant into the natural environment, for example by sanitation;
5. Massive problem: impossible to dilute or isolate, and essential to find effective ways to prevent pollutant escape.

Partly giving up

Korkman (1996) reports that the widespread problems of groundwater pollution in Denmark have brought the authorities to the conclusion that the present policy, that all groundwater should be protected, will have to change. The Danish government has decided on a priority ranking of the remedial actions necessary to protect and restore groundwater resources. Highest priority is given to 'areas of particular drinking water interest'. Chemical waste dumps and abandoned petrol filling-station sites should receive remedial treatment within 10 years, but there will never be sufficient money to remedy all contaminated areas. The costs of the necessary integrated water management systems are estimated to be an order of magnitude greater than Denmark has previously experienced.

As already indicated, it will be difficult to change the situation because the solution deeply affects the freedom of land owners and users, especially in certain countries and cultures. Their rights must often be reduced to prevent water pollution.

Understanding is essential for taking counter-measures

The best available information and the balance of scientific evidence clearly shows the scale of the water pollution problems and of the effort required both to take care of the burden of the past and to improve environmental quality. The possibility of taking proactive measures depends critically on public awareness and support from the general public. Therefore, awareness of both the problem and the scale of action required must be improved: as expressed by the Executive Director of the European Environment Agency, 'Facts are facts, but perception is reality'.

Because groundwater is invisible and its recharge is very poorly understood by the general public, a major awareness-raising effort must be part of the strategies chosen to address the massive problem of freshwater pollution in Europe, whether manifested or still hidden. The basic principles for water quality genesis should form the basis for proative avoidance. The task is extremely difficult, not only owing to the chemical complexities but also because of the poor general understanding of water mobility in the underground landscape and its effects. It should be recalled that society has no problems with regard to other natural phenomena such as gravitation. It is essential to create a similar respect for the functions and continuous mobility of water—a unique solvent, chemically active and with continuous movement through the landscape, above and below the ground. To this end, forceful educational programmes at all levels in society should be developed.

Visualization is helpful in facilitating an understanding of what takes place under the ground surface. In Denmark, where water supply relies totally on groundwater, large efforts have been made to clarify the risk of groundwater pollution from land-based pollution sources. The 'pollution flags' in Figure 3 have been constructed from the location of contaminant sources in the landscape and postulates of the subsurface water flow pattern based on the topography. The aim is to allow the general public to visualize where

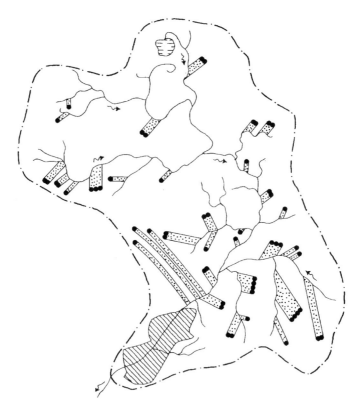

Figure 3. Visualization with 'pollution flags', showing location of sources (black) and stream tubes threatened by pollution from these sources (stippled). Urban polluting land-based activities (leaky wastewater network and oil tanks, polluting land-based activities; hatched). Idea from the Danish Environmental Authority. (From Falkenmark & Allard (1989).)

one might expect groundwater pollution from waste dumps and polluting activities in the landscape.

   Vulnerability maps are useful to permit the prediction of future risks of chemical time bombs in Europe. Land-use vulnerability of soils to physical and chemical degradation such as erosion, salinization and absorption of chemicals can be demonstrated with overlays of atmospheric, aquatic and land-based sources of pollutants, and linked with types of land use (Hekstra 1995).

Recommended research needs

Some key components to be studied further are the following:

- **identification of recharge areas** in the landscape of important raw water sources that need protection from polluting land-based activities;
- development of effective methods for **integrated planning of land use and water management;**
- development and adaptation of **visualization tools** such as the Danish pollution flags to real-world situations in different parts of Europe;
- development of methods for **vulnerability mapping** related to different sets of pollution threats such as acidification, chemical bombs, water-table changes and climate change;

- development of methods of **industrial metabolism** to cope better with the growing threat from consumer pollution (leaching of discarded consumer products);
- development of **better targeted fertilizers and pesticides** with less risk of incorporation into passing water;
- development and introduction of the science **'environmentology' in all university education** (FRN 1998) to produce a new, more flexible generation of professionals with a more holistic understanding of key relations between human activities and the life support systems in the European landscape;
- development of effective educational programmes that **raise awareness** among the general public and politicians;
- development of the **sense of ethics** and human responsibilities in business, farming and local communities.

Concluding remarks

When discussing a transition to sustainable consumption in regard to freshwater, a major challenge is the widely polluted groundwater in Europe, basically irreversible in the time scale of a human lifetime. This raises the question of the credibility of the contemplated EU Water Directive with its goal to achieve good groundwater status in all aquifers in a given period. The reality is one of prohibitive costs to remedy contaminated areas, on the one hand, and agricultural systems that continue to release nutrients and pesticides, and inadequate methods of solving that problem, on the other hand.

Except for the introduction of sewage systems to avoid water-related diseases, the main strategy in Europe has largely been to wait for scientifically well-documented damage on ecosystems before decisive moves have been decided towards minimizing the output of harmful substances from land to water systems. The key arguments used have referred to the protection of rather abstract ecosystems and their biodiversity, arguments that are frequently difficult to understand in the business sector.

The problem of pharmaceutical remnants and endocrine disruptors in water, originating from a wide array of chemical substances, is now causing an increasing alarm that human health and even fertility might be threatened. What might be emerging is a new understanding that everything water-soluble will end up in water and that human health might be threatened by micropollutants, both in the water and in the water-produced food consumed. A move towards sustainable consumption has to include blocking of the entry of health-hazard-causing chemicals into groundwater and river water.

In conclusion, the present stress on damage to diffuse ecological systems must be complemented with a strong emphasis on sustainable water consumption to protect human health and fertility.

References

European Environment Agency 1995 *Dobris assessment. Europe's environment.* Copenhagen: European Environment Agency.

European Environment Agency 1996 *The European Environment Agency. Europe's environment: status and trends.* Report by Executive Director to Danish Parliament, 3 October 1996.

Falkenmark, M. & Allard, B. 1989 Water quality genesis and disturbances of natural freshwaters. In *The handbook of environmental chemistry*, vol 5, part A (Water pollution) (ed. O. Hutzinger), pp. 45–78. Berlin: Springer-Verlag.

FRN 1998. *How to cope with degrading groundwater quality in Europe* (international workshop at Johannesberg, Sweden, in October 1997). Swedish Council for Planning and Coordination of Research (FRN) Report no. 98:4 (ed. T. Hilding-Rydevik & I. Johansson). Stockholm: FRN.

Hekstra, G.P. 1995 *Delayed effects of pollutants in soils and sediments: understanding and handling of chemical time bombs in Europe*. Ecoscript 56. Amsterdam: Stichting Mondiaal Alternatief.

Kobus, H. 1996. Water supply from groundwater resources and ecology: issues and controversies. In *Proceedings, NATO Advanced Research Workshop, Visegrad, Hungary, May 1996*, pp. 27–42 Budapest: Vituki.

Korkman, T.-E. 1996 Groundwater for the next generation. In *Stockholm Water Symposium 1996*. Stockholm: Stockholm Water Company, pp. 33–45.

Further reading

Eriksson, E. 1985 *Principles and applications of hydrochemistry*. London: Chapman & Hall.

European Environment Agency 1997 *Water stress in Europe—can the challenges be met?* Delivered as speeches at Copenhagen and Nairobi: EEA and UNEP respectively.

Sustainable agricultural production

Francesco Salamini

Department of Plant Breeding and Yield Physiology, Max-Planck Institut für Zuchtungsforschung, Carl-von-Linne-Weg 10, D-50829 Köln, Germany

Introduction

Several socio-economic indicators highlight the fact that patterns of food and feed production and use are changing rapidly. The most obvious trends include: changes in diet composition, with an emphasis on meat-based diets increasing demand for grain; accelerated rates of urbanization in low-income developing countries; increased scarcity of water and its inappropriate allocation; the relationship between the volume of world cereal stocks, commodity prices and levels of aid donation; and the failure of food production for political reasons (Pinstrup-Andersen *et al*. 1997; Dyson 1999). Furthermore, farm yields in parts of Asia are approaching optimum levels. These trends imply (1) that wider fluctuations in food production and prices are to be expected, and (2) that vulnerable developing countries will be exposed to higher risks of food insecurity.

Population increase and food needs

Long-term forecasts indicate that the population in 2020 of 7.7 billion people (3.5 billion of whom will be concentrated in urban areas) can be fed only by significantly increasing the production of cereals (+ 41%), meat (+ 63%) and roots and tubers (+ 40%). Much of this additional food will need to be produced in developing countries for their fast-expanding populations (Europe's population is declining) (Pinstrup-Andersen *et al*. 1997; Dyson 1999; Johnson 1999; Socolow 1999). The global requirements for maize, wheat and rice, respectively, will increase by 1.4%, 1.3% and 1.2% per year. Moreover, this increase in demand is expected to originate particularly in developing countries (+80% cereals; +90% meat; +90% tubers). For various reasons, food supply in these countries cannot be improved by increasing imports. It is also predicted that during the next 20 years 5.5% more virgin soil will be brought under the plough and devoted to cereal production (+39 Mha). Hence, in the same period, the yield of cereals (which represent about two-thirds of the total energy in human diets) has to reach a mean world level of $4\,t\,ha^{-1}$ (Cassman 1999; Dyson 1999; Tilman 1999). A critical consideration of the situation has directed attention to the need to double the yield again or to repeat the 'Green Revolution' (Mann 1999). In reality, the best global estimate of food availability in 2020 is 2900 kcal per person per day (2700 kcal in 1995) (1 kcal = 4.18 kJ), but sub-Saharan Africa will have only 2300 kcal at its disposal on average (a figure that does not reflect maldistribution). The conclusion is that in the year 2020 the food available in developing countries will not match the demand, particularly in respect of cereal production. A future shortfall in food availability can be also predicted from the trend of total grain production, which in recent years has been fairly steady at *ca.* 1900 Mt.

Cereal production

Considerations of the sustainability of food production must focus particularly on cereal cultivation, given the dominant role of these crops in agricultural systems. The intensification of wheat, rice and maize cropping systems has been largely responsible for a doubling in food production in the past 35 years, meaning that shortfalls in food supply have been avoided. This increase was associated with a 6-fold increase in nitrogen fertilization, a 3.5-fold increase in phosphorus use, a 1.7-fold increase in the area of irrigated land and a 1.1-fold increase in cultivated land. A second doubling of global food production will require an additional increase of nitrogen input by 2–3-fold, and a doubling of the area of irrigated land (to 32% of total agricultural land). According to Cassman (1999), the major cereal production systems include (1) irrigated double- and triple-crop rice in tropical and subtropical Asia in each year, (2) irrigated rice—wheat double cropping in northern India, Pakistan, Nepal and southern China in each year, (3) temperate rain-fed maize cropping in North America, and (4) the favourable rain-fed wheat systems of northern and central Europe. Other cropping systems exist in cereal-producing regions of the world in ecological environments similar to those of the regions cited. Both past and future agriculture intensification have had, and will have, further detrimental impacts on non-agricultural ecosystems, both terrestrial and aquatic. An urgent need is therefore emerging for more sustainable and efficient agricultural practices. The four major systems cited are already highly productive, but whether they are also sustainable is uncertain.

Ecological impacts of doubling food production

Fertilizers

For nitrogen fertilization, the projected need is to increase the use of N2 by at least 100% (Smil 1997). Food production already dominates the anthropogenic alteration of the nitrogen cycle, generating an excess of fixed nitrogen. The current rate of nitrogen fixation is twice that in pre-industrial times (300 Mt of nitrogen fixed per year, 120 Mt from industrial synthesis of fertilizers and biological fixation by plants; 40 Mt from high-temperature combustion). Nitrogen fixation increases the concentration of nitrous oxide in the atmosphere, which is 10% higher today than it was 100 years ago. Fixed nitrogen is problematic, because (1) nitrous oxide is a greenhouse gas (the fourth after water vapour, carbonic anhydride and methane), (2) nitrous oxide depletes stratospheric ozone and contributes to air pollution, (3) nitrogen ions in drinking water have negative effects on health, (4) atmospheric nitrous oxide contributes to acid rain, and (5) an increase in nitrate leads to the eutrophication of aquatic ecosystems and to decreases in biodiversity in terrestrial ecosystems.

Soil erosion and phosphate leakage

Agriculturally induced soil erosion has significant effects on crop productivity, particularly in some regions of the world. Erosion of topsoil and surface flow of water rich in phosphate contribute to the eutrophication of aquatic ecosystems. Data are available that address the quantitative impact of phosphate leakage from agricultural systems and define soil phosphate levels for optimum yield.

Soil degradation

This corresponds to a decrease in soil quality owing to human activities. The total area under threat is estimated to be 2000 Mha. Primary causes of degradation are overgrazing, deforestation and inappropriate farming practices. Degradation coexists with soil erosion in 84% of the total area considered, and is more evident in dry regions that are poorly suited to intensive agriculture. The phenomenon of yield decrease observed in long-term experiments with annual double- and triple-crop irrigated rice systems reflects a subtle form of soil degradation (Barnett *et al.* 1995).

Water scarcity

At present, 34 countries (with nearly 500 million inhabitants) suffer from water stress, and all but two are net importers of grain. In 2025 the number of countries with problems in water supply and use will increase to 50 (3 billion people). In 2050, from 3.5 billion to 7.7 billion people (depending on different population projections) will live in countries that are short of water. This will inevitably result in competition for water between agriculture and other activities.

Climate change

This is due, in part at least, to agricultural activity (methane and nitrous oxide emissions). The global warming trend is clear (an increase of between 1 and 3.5 °C in the mean annual global surface temperature is forecast by 2100). More data on the global and regional effects of temperature increase on agroecosystems are necessary (for examples see Watson *et al.* (1998)). Rising sea level will have effects on coastal agriculture, but agriculture can sometimes have a beneficial role in carbon sequestration.

Biodiversity

It will be difficult to double food production per unit of land without interfering with world biodiversity, particularly in more developed countries. Additional irrigation will severely limit water supply to aquatic ecosystems. The subtraction of land from terrestrial ecosystems will also negatively influence overall biodiversity. Nitrogen and phosphorus leakage from cultivated soils, while generating eutrophication of water, will contribute substantially to decreasing biological diversity (Tilman 1999).

Poverty in rural areas

Poverty in rural districts, arising from population density, production deficits, climate, catastrophes, low incomes and fragile soils, will lead to environmental degradation. The effects of poverty, in part due to agricultural intensification based on forest burning, excess grazing and use of water, generate several of the negative results already mentioned.

The foreseeable ecological impacts of doubling food production imply that more of the same does not work (Tilman 1999). Nevertheless, agriculture will need to remain intensive on all continents of the world because the alternatives involve further encroachment on forests and the agricultural use of marginal soils.

Achieving sustainability

The need for improved knowledge

To introduce efficient measures that favour sustainability in agricultural production, particularly in intensive cereal cultivation systems, we need better global and regional agronomic information. The management of water quality in agriculture is still little more than a perceived need. The same holds for crop protection. As is well known, the Green Revolution induced an increase in the use of pesticides. To counteract this trend, integrated pest management (IPM) was introduced, a concept that is becoming more popular. It assumes a decrease in pesticide use, the biocontrol of insect and microorganism epidemics, breeding for plant resistance and the adoption of adapted cultural techniques. A number of IPM systems are in use; however, they have not been markedly successful (Lenteren 1998). This should be a matter for concern, and studies on the practical application of IPM in agriculture (or the reasons for their failure) are an urgent necessity. A concept similar to IPM, termed integrated nutrient management, is being developed for fertilizer use.

Even more has to be done to define principles and rules for the ecological intensification of agriculture. This concept is vague and open to more precise scientific quantification. For example, the rate of disease development or pest outbreak depends on the density of the host population (Tilman 1999). This generates a need to define the role of the diversity of crops attacked in a region, of substitute crops, and of genetic resistance within crops. In addition, the idea that the stability of primary productivity is greater in ecosystems that contain a greater diversity of plants needs further investigation before it can assume practical relevance (Daily 1997; Mooney & Mooney 1994; Tilman & Downing 1994). In general, a better understanding of how the different components of ecosystems function, and how their ecological contributions can be protected while moving to more intensive land use, are primary needs. This will mean placing basic ecology at the heart of sustainability in crop production. The problem with this approach is that we might not have sufficient time to put efficient strategies in place.

More research is needed on plant diversity to improve our understanding of the following: the positive and negative elements of monocultures; to assess rates of loss of nutrients, or their accumulation in agroecosystems; to understand yield decline in long-term intensive agricultural cultivation and the reasons for such declines; to describe the complexity of the relationships between soil quality and cropping system performance; and to identify critical thresholds for soil properties that have the greatest influence on productivity, such as levels of soil salinization. An area that is almost untouched is the modelling of sustainable livestock development. In general, predictive, mechanistic models of the impact of agriculture on natural ecosystems are still a necessity. Given that mechanisms of pest reduction in ecosystems are virtually unknown, it is difficult to model this area without further studies devoted to describing population dynamics.

Rasmussen *et al.* (1988) claims that it is necessary to set up standards for long-term agroecosystem experiments that study crop production, nutrient cycling and environmental impacts of agriculture. In general, basic studies on drought and desertification and on the biological fixation of nitrogen should also contribute to long-term sustainability of agriculture.

The need for action

Decreasing the chemical support of intensive agriculture is not an easy task. Indeed, the opposite is expected by 2020, namely a doubling of nitrogen fertilizer usage. Precision agriculture provides a practical, albeit still very sophisticated, approach, to ensure that resources for crop growth are available and crop protection needs are met without deficiency or excess, thus efficiently controlling the distribution of fertilizers (Matson *et al.* 1997).

One obvious issue in sustainability concerns the improvement of the efficiency of food production. Of the 120 Mt of nitrogen which are added to soils each year, only 50% ends up in harvested crops; of this quantity, only one-half is directly ingested by humans. Zero-loss systems have been proposed based on systems that also return nitrogen to the soil. However, these systems are too unrealistic to be adopted, having throughput yields resembling those of pre-industrial times. The control of nitrogen conservation in manure, the better use of human wastes, the adoption of nitrogen and phosphorus management strategies more responsive to the environment and public health, and the control of protein level in diets are all measures that seem more promising in the shorter term. Shifting diets towards the consumption of more plant calories and proteins is an additional measure that would support the sustainability of food production.

Soil erosion can be efficiently counteracted by minimum tillage practices. The problem is that such an approach to sustainability of soil fertility might work well for one crop but not for another. Moreover, social and economic circumstances still prevail in the choice of viable options for soil management. In the long term, however, and particularly for continuous cropping systems, available methods of soil fertility conservation need to be adopted (Reeves 1997).

Given that pests and diseases cause losses of 30–40% in crop production, the increased use of biopesticides in agriculture is a possibility, especially in view of their comparative neglect at present (they account for less than 1% of the total crop protection market (Lisansky 1997)). However, if microbial control agents or biopesticides are to move out of niche markets a better understanding of host–parasite biology is required.

The core action, which could readily be implemented, is to ask for more radical scientific solutions capable of contributing new agricultural systems, intensive but nevertheless sustainable (Cassman 1999; Mann 1999; Pinstrup-Andersen *et al.* 1997; Tilman 1999). The emerging concept is that whereas in the past we have made significant efforts to adapt the environment to the plant, new crops should be bred that use less nitrogen and water, are resistant if not immune to diseases and pests, give high yields and are more adapted to human and animal nutrition. Conventional plant breeding still has a major role in providing crop varieties. In plant breeding, heritability of traits can be made efficient by the use of molecular markers linked to the genes supporting a useful trait. Thus, the adoption of marker-assisted selection permits the selection of single traits with favourable heritability values. These methods are now being replaced by a more integrated approach based on the capacity to direct and monitor the evolution of crop genomes at the level of the structure, function, location and expression of large numbers of genes.

Biotechnology is also an indispensable tool, and its adoption in plant breeding, particularly in the tropics and subtropics, might become a necessity (Krattiger 1998; Vasil 1998). Effective insect control can be achieved by using transgenic crops that express insecticidal proteins. This approach is by far the most successful contribution of plant biotechnology to agriculture in developed countries, but it is also important for developing countries. However, if risks are associated with the use of insecticidal transgenic plants (Halweil 1999), they will have to be evaluated thoroughly. The successful protection of transgenics against plant viral attack has already been reported for 20 crops infected by more than 30 viruses.

A second group of gene technologies addresses the improvement of the nutrient value of food and feed. Examples are the enrichment of human foods with β-carotene to correct vitamin A deficiency in diets; increases in levels of phytosterols, which have the capacity to reduce cholesterol loads in humans; the improvement of the caloric density of grain by enhancing oil or starch content; the enhancement of lysine and tryptophan levels in cereal and of sulphur-containing amino acids in legume seeds; the production of oils with special saturated and unsaturated fatty acids; and the improvement of feed utilization based on high-level expression of cellulase, phospholipase and toxin-degrading enzymes. One special use of transgenic crops opens the possibility of obtaining mass immunization against infective diseases by preparing edible oral vaccines.

The role of biotechnology in providing solutions to agricultural sustainability is under intense debate, particularly in Europe. The emerging position is that issues such as the ethical dimension and public acceptability should become an integral part of a process leading to the adoption of this technology (The Royal Society 1999).

The need to decide

Government policy in developed and developing countries should contribute to modifying the present trends in agricultural production. Governments need to design policies and legislative frameworks in the following areas: water management (although it will be difficult to introduce institutionalized management arrangements to encourage the more efficient use of water); property rights in land and natural resources; earning opportunities and welfare supports for low-income farmers; energy management in agriculture; and rural infrastructures. However, many actions relevant to sustainability in food production can be implemented only in an international context. These actions should address the following issues: the need to keep cereal stocks constant (which beneficially influences market prices and the global level of production); the definition of region-specific and crop-specific fertilizer inputs; the intensification of technology flow between the private and public sectors; decisions on food aid to support and/or regulate long-term plans for food imports; facilitation of the participation of rural communities in the market economy; and the allocation of investment capital to world development.

The last issue is of particular relevance. The present levels of investment, particularly in research directed to sustainability, are not adequate to meet the challenge (Cassman 1999). However, the trend of official development finance is declining and this needs to be reversed. In addition, the flow of private capital into investments deserves attention: the two poorest world regions, sub-Saharan Africa and southern Asia, attract only 10% of net private capital flow at present.

Focusing on agricultural research and on technology transfer offers additional opportunities. Productivity in agricultural research is declining: that is, to achieve the same effects, more time and more investment are required per unit output. The hope is that biotechnology-based research will reverse this trend, even where intellectual property rights complicate the issue. Simulations show that the delayed diffusion of biotechnology to developing countries—the 'modern' approach to agricultural research—can exacerbate food crises. Agricultural expansion and improvements in training are also primary components in the flow of technology from research to farmer. The involvement of the consumer and the citizen should also help to enhance the acceptability of the results of agricultural research (Socolow 1999).

The transition to agricultural sustainability

Although soil degradation and water-related problems represent serious constraints, the drive for agriculture sustainability during the twenty-first century will take place alongside the need for sustainable populations and levels of material consumption. Optimistic and pessimistic models have been proposed for the trajectory of the transition. A primary defence against uncertainties along the road to achieving a stable accommodation between agricultural and environmental imperatives is agricultural research capacity. Nevertheless, if we fail to meet the goal, the reasons will lie more in the area of institutional innovation and in the use of resources to eliminate environmental constraints.

It is already evident that an ecologically viable intensification of agriculture will not be characterized by a return to forms of low-input–low-output agriculture typical of pre-industrial times (Avery 1994). In comparison with 1967, the land area devoted to maize cultivation has expanded by more than 30 Mha. If the yield per unit of land had remained at the 1967 level, an additional 446 Mha of land would have been necessary to achieve present world output. This example shows that low-input agriculture favours the occupation of natural ecosystems and marginal land, thus adding to ground- and surface-water pollution, decreasing biodiversity and perturbing carbon and nitrogen cycles. However, in regions where high-input, ecologically intensified agriculture is difficult to introduce, specific policies have to be established to expand local productivity. It should also be emphasized that reintroducing organic food production would result, in the short run, in a sharp decrease in productivity, a situation only sustainable if the whole world were to adopt vegetarian diets. Moreover, the proponents of organic low-input agriculture frequently see agricultural research more as a problem than a solution (Pinstrup-Andersen *et al.* 1997). This generates the belief that it is not necessary to increase food production, a belief that in the long term may negatively affect global food supply.

A more reasoned transition has to consider alternative solutions adapted to local conditions. For unfavourable rain-fed environments, the central role of cereals can be decreased by livestock production, crop diversification, agroforestry or the adoption of reduced-till technologies. Systems in which the potential for yield improvement exists (where yields are less than 70% of yield potential), as in favourable irrigated regions, provide the greatest opportunity for an intensified form of agriculture.

Sustainability of agricultural production as seen from Europe

Agricultural intensification has received particular support in Europe. This has stimulated studies on the sustainability of available systems of food production. In this respect, Europe can share with the rest of the world its experience and knowledge, particularly in terms of the ecological conditions of central and northern regions. These conditions should allow sustainable annual crop cultivation. However, the development of integrated arable production systems to meet environmental requirements is a European priority (Jordan 1998). Thus, farming in Europe is integrated in respect of a market system based on financial profits, a situation that in part complicates the implementation of sustainable systems. If we consider that nearly 40% of total European grain production is fed to animals, it is reasonable to assume that European agricultural policy still has options available for the establishment of new agricultural systems.

Plant nutrient management can still be improved in Europe, including the northern and central parts of the continent. Opportunities to decrease levels of applied nitrogen should result from researches on the measurement and time-course of nitrogen flow, emission and mineralization. It is nevertheless true that a tradition exists in Europe that is concerned with investigating the sustainability of fertilizer balance in soils, with model-based explorations of farming systems in specific countries, and decision-support models to provide long-term predictions in tree cultivation. New agroforestry systems, as well as soil-less sustainable greenhouse horticulture, are two recent examples of what is proposed to anticipate land-use change. In the same region, the maintenance of healthy soil and water seems fundamental to future agricultural production (Jordan 1998). One example of a less intensive integrated agricultural system is the Life project. According to Jordan (1998), this hierarchical, integrated, arable crop production experiment involves multifunctional crop rotation, minimal soil cultivation, integrated nutrient management and crop protection, and ecological infrastructure management. The results of the first phase of the Life project indicate that, on the basis of a decrease in applied nitrogen (-36%), herbicides (-26%), fungicides (-79%) and pesticides (-78%), production costs were cut by 34%, with a loss of only 12% in yield. In countries of southern Europe, the assessment of the components and economics of sustainable dryland farming systems needs better modelling. This will contribute to improve local situations but will also provide knowledge that is applicable to developing subtropical countries.

References

Avery, D.T. 1994 Saving the planet with high-yield farming. In *49th Annual Corn and Sorghum Research Conference*, ed. D.B. Wilkinson, pp. 1–12. Indianapolis: The Hudson Institute.

Barnett, V., Payne, R. & Steiner, R. (eds) 1995 *Agricultural sustainability in economic, environmental and statistical considerations*. Chichester: Wiley.

Cassman, K.G. 1999 Ecological intensification of cereal production systems: yield potential, soil quality, and precision agriculture. *Proceedings of the National Academy of Sciences, USA* **96**, 5952–5959.

Daily, G. (ed.) 1997 *Nature's services: Societal dependence on natural ecosystems*. Washington, DC: Island Press.

Dyson, T. 1999 World food trends and prospects to 2050. *Proceedings of the National Academy of Sciences, USA* **96**, 5929–5936.

Halweil, B. 1999 The emperor's new crops. *World-Watch* (July/August), pp. 21–29.

Johnson, D.G. 1999 The growth of demand will limit output growth for food over the next quarter century. *Proceedings of the National Academy of Sciences, USA* **96**, 5915–5920.

Jordan, V.W.L. 1998 The development of integrated arable production systems to meet potential economic and environmental requirements. *Outlook on Agriculture* **27**, 145–151.

Krattiger, A. 1998 *The importance of Ag-biotech to global prosperity*. ISAAA Briefs no. 6. Ithaca, NY: ISAAA.

Lenteren, J.C. van 1998 Sustainable and safe crop protection: a reality? *Mededelingen-Faculteit Landbouwkundige en Toegepaste Biologische Wetenschappen Universiteit Gent* **63**, 409–414.

Lisansky, S. 1997 Microbial biopesticides. *British Crop Protection Council Symposium Proceedings* **68**, 3–10.

Mann, C.M. 1999 Crop scientists seek a new revolution. *Science* **283**, 310–314.

Matson, P.A., Parton, W.J., Power, A.G. & Swift, M.J. 1997 Agricultural intensification and ecosystem properties. *Science* **277**, 504–509.

Mooney, E.-D. & Mooney, H.A. (eds) 1994 *Biodiversity and ecosystem function*. Berlin: Springer-Verlag.

Pinstrup-Andersen, P., Pandaya-Lorsch, R. & Rosegrant, M.W. 1997 The world food situation: Recent developments, emerging issues, and long-term prospects, 2020. 2020 Vision Food Policy Report. Washington DC: International Food Policy Research Institute (IFPRI).

Rasmussen, P.E., Goulding, K.W.T., Brown, J.R., Grace, P.R., Janzen, H.H. & Korschens, M. 1998 Agroecosystem—long-term agroecosystem experiments—assessing agricultural sustainability and global change. *Science* **282**, 893–896.

Reeves, D.W. 1997 The role of soil organic matter in maintaining soil quality in continuous cropping systems. *Soil and Tillage Research* **43**, 131–167.

The Royal Society 1999 *GMOs and the environment*. London: The Royal Society.

Smil, V. 1997 Global population and the nitrogen cycle. *Scientific American* **277**, 58–63.

Socolow, R.H. 1999 Nitrogen management and the future of food: lessons from the management of energy and carbon. *Proceedings of the National Academy of Sciences, USA* **96**, 6001–6008.

Tilman, D. 1999 Global environmental impacts of agricultural expansion: the need for sustainable and efficient practices. *Proceedings of the National Academy of Sciences, USA* **96**, 5995–6000.

Tilman, D. & Downing, J.A. 1994 Biodiversity and stability in grasslands *Nature* **367**, 363–365.

Vasil, I.K. 1998 Biotechnology and food security for the 21st century: a real-world perspective. *Nature Biotechnology* **16**, 399–400.

Watson, R.T., Zinyowera, M.C., Moss, R.H. & Dokken, D.J. 1998 *The regional impacts of climate change. An assessment of vulnerability*. Cambridge University Press.

The role of technology in sustainable consumption

Gábor Náray-Szabó

Hungarian Academy of Sciences, Department of Theoretical Chemistry, Lorand Eotvos University, Pazmany Peter Street 1A, H-1117 Budapest, Hungary

Introduction

Supported by the spectacular progress of technology that occurred in the nineteenth century, some analysts insist that this is the key component in the very complex process of transition to a sustainable world. Its role should be to reduce the environmental impact on each person and in terms of cost of economic activity. However, we must recognize that technology alone cannot solve problems that are linked mainly to human behaviour, namely unsustainable consumption patterns and a lack of environmental awareness. The overestimation of the role of technology is due mainly to the exponentially increasing number of isolated success stories linked to technology that are well known to the decision-makers as well as the public, and are not completed with the necessary mental and societal evolution. This controversy should be stressed to avoid exaggerated expectations that are necessarily followed by reduced support.

There are two basic arguments against technology. First, its success is self-defeating: if we solve problems, our population (and consumption) will grow and create further, and eventually insurmountable, problems. Public-health measures and modern medicine diminish mortality, whereas fertility declines at a much slower pace, leading to explosions in population and consumption. It should be stressed that the cardinal case is not population growth in developing countries but increasing consumption in the industrialized world, challenging less developed nations to keep pace. The second argument against technology is that it creates weapons that kill. We can use science and technology to provide goods and services for human comfort, but technology serves both constructive and destructive purposes. Some would feel more comfortable with less of the latter. For the survival of mankind, however, this comfort should be combined with decreasing and reasonable consumption of the non-renewable resources of our planet.

This paper discusses some major issues of a transition to sustainability, in which technology has a major role. I shall focus on those aspects that are linked to the design, production and use of new materials and the application of new technological processes or the reformulation of old ones. It should be stressed that the concept of sustainability implies a very complex, holistic and interdisciplinary approach and a wide variety of disciplines, ranging from physics and chemistry to process engineering, economics, computer and environmental sciences; even sociology and psychology are involved. Thus, we are forced to make an attempt to shed light on various aspects of the problem; this might eventually lead to contradictions. My discussion will be based on the concept of industrial metabolism that seems to be part of the right answer to the global challenge that our society is facing.

Industrial metabolism

The concept of sustainability can be illustrated by natural ecosystems that function as closed cycles involving slow changes. In all these systems, changes usually occur at a pace that allows time for the adaptation of the natural environment. In contrast, technology has so far used a linear approach (Figure 1). Resources have been extracted as though they were inexhaustible, and they are processed by industry in an unlimited way to make synthetic products that have no natural counterparts. Finally, both raw materials and manufactured products are transported to industrial plants or to the site of consumption. In each step a big impact is made on the environment and an increasing amount of waste is produced that has to be dealt with (Roberts 1994).

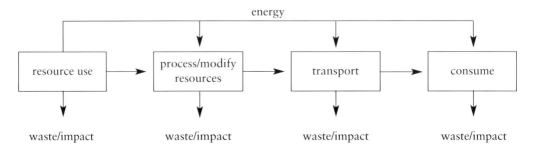

Figure 1. Linear system of industrial activity (Roberts 1994).

Sustainability will require the adoption of a system that models natural processes as displayed in Figure 2. Unlike the linear approach, the use, processing, transportation and consumption of resources and products must flow continuously as a closed loop to the extent possible, rather than as a linear system. The manner in which we process, modify and transport resources must be in harmony with the environment. It is crucial that consumer habits be changed, leading to lower waste production, a careful use of non-renewable resources, a reduction of the need for transport and a more even distribution of goods and

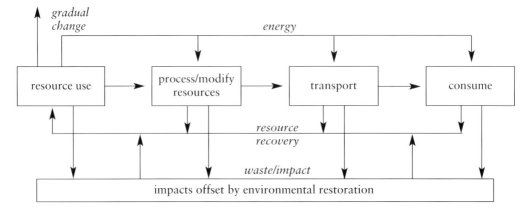

Figure 2. Sustainable system of industrial metabolism (Roberts 1994).

services. According to the 'zero emission' principle (Pauli 1998), we need ways to move from leaky to looped systems with plausible models for the transition from leaks to loops, especially for energy. Throughout technological processes the amount of waste must be minimized, by-products must be recycled repeatedly as recovered resources, and the rest should be in forms that have minimal long-term impact on the environment.

There are some simple principles that should be followed when redesigning a process or a product in the spirit of industrial metabolism. The concept of waste should be eliminated from industrial design. We need to design every process so that the products themselves, as well as leftover chemicals, materials and effluents, can be reused in other processes. We should expect that current solar income will diminish and eventually eliminate our reliance on hydrocarbon fuels. Furthermore, we should design systems that use energy at a reasonable pace. We need to evaluate every design for its impact on plant, animal and human life by considering immediate and long-term effects. An appealing example can be found in the Kalundborg industrial park in Denmark, where one company's waste becomes another's resource (Ehrenfeld & Gertler 1997). Waste reduction translates to US$120 million in savings and revenues on a US$60 million investment over a five-year period. More than 20 American cities plan to develop parks like that at Kalundborg.

Resources

It has become commonplace that the use of vital non-renewable resources should be minimized and our economy must turn towards renewable rather than non-renewable resources. However, it is not widely appreciated that renewable resources must be harvested only within the limits allowed by Nature: the pace of use of natural goods is therefore crucial. The rate of transformation of resources that is sustainable depends on the rate of natural regeneration, the capacity of the environment to assimilate effluents without substantial negative impact, and the rate at which more abundant alternatives can replace them. There are essentially two ways of filling the continuously increasing resource needs: reduction of consumption and increase in productivity. It seems that a radical change in the latter is unrealistic.

Beside taking market measures by increasing prices to reduce demand, a promising way of achieving a lower consumption of energy and mineral is 'dematerialization' of the economy, which means fostering efforts to deliver equal or better services with less input and energy (Kanoh 1992). This ambition is greatly supported by computerization, which allows companies to optimize and scale down industrial processes, reducing their consumption of energy and materials. The energy need of technological processes is reduced by computer-assisted process and control engineering that uses mathematical models of fundamental phenomena for the minimization of energy use in industrial plants. However, computers generate many new needs that might worsen the balance. For example, the widespread use of personal computers led to a considerable increase in the consumption of stationery, adding a further drive towards deforestation. Innovative technology should find an appropriate substitute for paper sheets used for the temporary storage of information from computers, to ensure sustainability.

We have large reserves from which to improve the effectiveness of processes that consume resources. For example, cars are only 1% efficient in the sense that, of every 100 litres of petrol, only 1 litre actually moves the passengers. Only 8–10% of the energy used in heating the filament of a light bulb becomes visible light. About 94% of the materials extracted for use in making durable products become waste before the product is even manufactured (Hawken *et al.* 1999). Overall, such examples show that the use of energy is no more than 1–2% efficient. Fortunately, we have several techniques that can reduce the use of resources. For example, the amount of timber and pulpwood can be reduced by nearly 75% without diminishing the quality of housing, the usefulness of books and paper or the convenience of a tissue. Miniaturization, made possible by computerization, allows the sparing of a large proportion of the resources used in the economy. New technologies, fans, lights, pumps, super-efficient windows, motors and other products, combined with intelligent mechanical and building design, could reduce energy consumption by 90% (Hawken *et al.* 1999). The application of fibre-reinforced concrete plaster for buildings needs to be only half as thick as simple concrete to make a durable surface, while being five times stronger (Myers 1997).

The increase in energy production should be shifted from non-renewable to renewable resources. An important concept is decarbonization, which decreases the amount of emitted carbon dioxide, which is mainly responsible for the greenhouse effect (Kanoh 1992). Decarbonization means the evolution of energy systems for more service while burning less carbon through more low-carbon fuel (natural gas) or no-carbon fuel (hydrogen) and through more efficient generation, distribution and use. Globally, over the past two centuries, a succession of primary sources has held the largest share of the energy market, first wood and hay (dominating until the 1870s), then coal (peaking in the 1920s), and oil (peaking in the 1970s). If the succession continues, natural gas will move ahead, peaking in *ca.* 2030 (Nakicenovic 1996). Thus, the H/C molar ratio increases continuously, from wood (H/C = 0.1), via coal (H/C = 1) and oil (H/C = 2) to natural gas (H/C = 4).

Photovoltaic modules offer a promising solution for the industrialized world, mainly in niche applications. However, they can also be applied in less developed countries as a cost-effective means of supplying simple homes with power for lighting, TV sets and basic tools. Between 1975 and 1998 the world photovoltaic shipment increased by almost two orders of magnitude from 1.8 MW in 1975 to 152 MW in 1998 (Brown *et al.* 1999)

Unfortunately, prospects for a purely commercial breakthrough suffer from the concurrent production of electricity generated from fossil fuels, which are subsidized ten times as much as clean and renewable sources of energy such as solar power. A further problem is the increasing price of the feedstock material for standard solar cells. Major increases are expected in wind energy (see Schoot Uiterkamp, this volume) and biomass gasification, as well as in geothermal energy generation. In 1997 the rate of growth in wind-energy capacity was 22% and totalled 7700 MW in the USA. Solar energy capacity was 600 MW. The debate on whether nuclear plants might replace fossil-generated electricity is still open (Royal Society and Royal Academy of Engineering 1999). Although nuclear electricity looks more attractive economically and in terms of carbon dioxide emissions, no final solution has been found for the permanent storage of spent nuclear fuels or the adverse social and psychological effects. The insulating capacity of construction materials is continually increased and architectures have been developed that more and more effectively prevent the escape of waste heat.

Designing and applying new materials with specific properties can reduce the need both for non-renewable minerals and renewable natural resources (Kelly 1998). Today we already have thousands of designed materials replacing metals (high-performance composites and organic conductors), wood (plastics), cotton, wool and linen (synthetic fibres). Freshwater use should also be reduced simultaneously with the development of efficient technologies for wastewater treatment and the desalination of seawater. The large energy need of the latter should therefore be reduced to provide a truly sustainable technology. Soil should be considered a vital resource, and industrial impacts should be reduced to a minimum. Soil erosion and acidification should be prevented by appropriate agricultural, environmental, technological, economic and legal measures.

Industrial processes

Technology must take the lead in redesigning existing industrial processes. This can be achieved by reducing the product weight by applying lighter materials and by careful design challenging materials sciences and process engineering. As a result of the ability to model processes and structures at the molecular level, a spectacular development in these fields could be observed. The weight/performance ratio of construction materials has radically improved in recent decades and a range of designer plastics, composites and alloys are now available that allow the design of lighter but better buildings, machines and consumables. Computerization is an integral part of the solution that permits much safer design in practically all fields of technology. Industries should concentrate more on satisfying wants (e.g. floor coverings) than selling products (e.g. carpets). This could reduce the amount of waste and simultaneously generate new jobs (Hawken *et al.* 1999). The life cycle of all products should be analysed, because until now this has been done for only a small number of products.

An example of the appropriate use of industrial processes in achieving sustainability is an 'evergreen carpet lease' programme. Today, 95% of carpet materials are based on petrochemicals and in the USA they end up in landfills at a rate of 4000 t per day. Modern carpeting remains on the floor for up to 12 years, after which it remains in landfills for as long as 20 000 years. This is less than 0.06% efficiency (Hawken *et al.* 1999). A multinational carpet and flooring company, Interface, has developed a system to transform its commercial product, carpet tiles, into a service by leasing to building owners. As carpet tiles wear and require replacement, they are recycled and transformed into new tiles as part of the lease fee. The customer pays no installation cost, but rather a monthly fee for constantly functional carpeting. In this way the company saved $96 million in four years by reducing waste.

Transport

It is well known that increased transport puts a heavy burden on the environment. It is therefore important to reduce unfounded needs for the movement of humans and goods, including a diminution in exaggerated tourism and the transport of half-manufactured goods and intermediates from one region to another, to reduce labour costs. Consequently, sustainable transport policy should be concerned not only with travel but also with lifestyles, time management of people, social interaction and electronic communication (Nijkamp *et al.* 1998). In contrast, technology should create low-energy transportation systems, and smaller cars should be made that operate more efficiently. Individual vehicles should be replaced with efficient mass transportation. Improved fuels need to be developed and exhaust systems perfected. The transportation of fuels by pipelines and ships needs to incorporate improved emergency control systems and more effective remediation procedures.

To foster the development of efficient vehicles with low consumption and low emissions, an entirely new car is under development by several companies all over the world. This 'hypercar' consists mostly of an extremely light carbon-fibre body that is safer than steel because it absorbs crash energy better (Lovins *et al.* 1996). It has a small engine, a gas turbine or fuel cell providing a constant source of electricity and variable-speed reversible electric motors that can recapture braking energy for reuse after temporary storage in a battery or super flywheel. Such a light, quiet, safe and 95% less polluting car would need an engine only one-tenth as large as a standard one. Transportation needs could be reduced by the better design of communities that could eliminate 40–60% of driving needs. Although internet-based transactions could render many shopping centres obsolete, it must be carefully examined whether the new system really needs less energy and has a lower impact on the environment than the old one.

Consumables

Technology should turn its attention towards consumables that put a smaller burden on the environment because they need less energy, can be recycled or are more durable. The throwaway attitude of the industrialized world, strongly supported by present consumer patterns and associated advertisement campaigns, will need to change. The future might provide diodes that emit light for 20 years without bulbs, ultrasound washing machines that use no water, heat or soap, lightweight materials that are stronger than steel, and reprintable paper (Hawken *et al.* 1999). Some biological technologies reduce or eliminate the need for insecticides and fertilizers; we have reusable and compostable plastics, and piezoelectric polymers that can generate electricity from shoe heels or the force of a wave by transforming pressure into electric power (Hawken *et al.* 1999). Taxation is an important method of supporting these products and processes.

Difficulties arise in connection with sophisticated materials and their applications. Alloys and composites with attractive structural properties can be hard to separate and recycle. Popular materials might be lighter but more toxic. The reuse of plastics might be less economical than burning them cleanly for fuel or otherwise extracting their chemical energy. Most important is that economic and population growth has multiplied the volume of products and objects, so that total wastes have tended to increase while declining per unit of economic activity (see Gardner & Sampat (1998) for more details).

Wastes

In the USA more waste is created than products (500 t per person per year). This figure does not account for waste generated outside the country. It has been estimated that for every 1 kg of product, 32 kg of waste is created. Less than 5% of the total waste is recycled, consisting primarily of paper, glass, plastic, aluminium and steel. The domestic waste per person in the European Union is 414 kg per year, in comparison with the OECD average of 510 kg per year. In the early 1990s the European Union was producing 27 Mt of hazardous wastes per year that required handling in some way. Formerly, part was exported to developing countries, where it was buried untreated but very cheaply, but by 1998 more than 100 countries had agreed to ban such exports.

An effective waste reduction might be achieved by following the fate of any product from initial design through development and production phases until consumption, waste formation and degradation occurs. New materials with longer lifetimes, better recycling properties and lower weight are needed to reach the above goals. Applying atom-to-atom processes in chemical industry can approach an ideal situation. In these processes each atom of the starting materials will be transformed to the desirable final products by the extensive use of specially designed catalysts.

Packaging makes up *ca.* 50% by volume of the solid-waste stream and should be composed of biological nutrients, or materials that can be thrown onto the ground or the compost heap to biodegrade. There is no need for packaging that persists for decades or even centuries and products should be designed at the very start to be recycled or returned to industrial systems with improved quality. By now, several companies around the world are producing 100% biodegradable plastics (McDonough & Braungart 1998).

Recycling diminishes the demand for primary materials and can be considered a form of dematerialization. It regained standing as a generalized social practice in those industrialized countries with enormous appetites for metals. At Xerox, world-wide recycling operations have boosted profits by US$200 million during three recent years, and by US$700 million over the whole period of the process. The company's latest 'green-designed' photocopiers with every part reusable or recyclable are expected to save US$1 billion through long-term remanufacturing (Hawken *et al.* 1999).

A specific task is the breakdown and safe storage of hazardous wastes. The primary goal is to reduce their amount by careful design; however, they cannot be fully eliminated from industry. Incineration in high-temperature ovens, in combination with concrete production or melting into glass bricks that release only negligible amounts within the foreseeable future, might provide a solution in the long term. Hazardous wastes often contain valuable compounds that could be used as a starting material for industrial processes.

Conclusions

Technology, although not omnipotent, can help greatly in sustaining reasonable consumption and allowing the less developed nations to catch up with the industrialized world. The principle of industrial metabolism should be followed, in which processes flow as continuously closed loops rather than open linear systems. Designed materials can replace non-renewable resources, and renewable resources should be exploited only at a pace that Nature allows. Materials science is an area in which sustainable consumption has become more of a reality and it points the way towards a more sustainable future. It has enabled us to do 'more with less', making better use of lighter materials and stressing the importance of recycling. Consumption patterns should be changed to reduce the amount of waste, energy and material used, while maintaining the desired human comfort.

References

Brown, L.R., Renner, M. & Halweil, B. 1999 *Vital signs 1999*. New York: Norton.

Ehrenfeld, J. & Gertler, N. 1997 Industrial ecology in practice. The evolution of interdependence at Kalundborg. *Journal of Industrial Ecology* 1, 67–79.

Gardner, G. & Sampat, P. 1998 *Mind over matter. Recasting the role of materials in our lives*. Washington, DC: Worldwatch Institute.

Hawken, P., Lovins, A. & Lovins, L.H. 1999 *Natural capitalism*. London: Earthscan.

Kanoh, T, 1992 Toward dematerialization and decarbonization. In *Science and sustainability*, pp. 63–94. Vienna: International Institute of Applied Systems Analysis.

Kelly, A. 1998 Materials science. *Interdisciplinary Science Review* 23, 321–324.

Lovins, A.B., Brylawski, M.M., Cramer, D.R. & Moore, T.C. 1996 *Hypercars: materials, manufacturing, and policy implications*. Snowmass, Colorado: Rocky Mountain Institute.

McDonough, W. & Braungart, M. 1998 The next industrial revolution. *Atlantic Monthly* 282 (4) 82–92.

Myers, N. 1997 Our forestry prospect: the past recycled or a surprise-rich future? *The Environmentalist* 17, 233–247.

Nakicenovic, N. 1996 Freeing energy from carbon. *Daedalus* 125 (3) 95–112.

Nijkamp, P., Rienstra, S. & Vleugel, J. 1998 *Transportation planning and the future*. New York: Wiley.

Pauli, G. 1998 *The road to zero emissions: more jobs, more income and no pollution*. Sheffield: Greenleaf.

Roberts, D.V. 1994 Sustainable development—a challenge for the engineering profession. In *The role of engineering in sustainable development* (ed. M.D. Ellis), pp. 44–61. Washington, DC: American Association of Engineering Societies.

Royal Society and Royal Academy of Engineering 1999 *Nuclear energy, the future climate*. London: The Royal Society and The Royal Academy of Engineering.

Drivers of consumption patterns

Laurie Michaelis

Oxford Centre for the Environment, Ethics and Society, Mansfield College, Oxford, OX1 3TF, UK

Introduction

It is often tempting to seek simple answers to our problems. The debate over what might be done to improve sustainability has often been reduced to a choice between three options: reducing population, reducing individual consumption (wealth), and improving the efficiency of production. Recently, the political debate has become rather more sophisticated and it is recognized that concurrent efforts are needed to develop the conditions for demographic stability, to reduce the pollution and resource intensity of production and consumption, and perhaps also to encourage a shift in consumption patterns. The emphasis in the latter is on 'consuming differently, rather than less'.

Specialists from several academic disciplines have developed theories of consumption and the forces that shape it—again, often seeking a single-driver model. As a result, there is a plethora of different explanations of consumption at the level of individuals, social groups and society as a whole.

The diversity of explanations is possible because material consumption is linked to almost every other aspect of our lives, for example: consumption patterns are related to economic development, technological change, institutions, landscapes, demographic distributions, education systems, communication systems, and cultures.

This paper attempts to make some sense of the confusion of connections, and to identify a few influences that might be particularly powerful. In the next section I start by giving a historical perspective on the emergence of modern consumption patterns and consumerism. With this context the following section (*Mechanisms shaping consumption*) identifies a number of factors that contribute to the shaping of consumption patterns; the final section (*Changing consumption patterns*) then turns to the processes that might contribute to the spread of a post-materialist, and even sustainable, culture.

The emergence of twentieth-century consumerism

Modern consumption patterns emerged from industrial development in North America and Europe, which in turn was shaped by many threads of change in Europe in the twelfth to eighteenth centuries. To give just a few examples, these included:

- the intellectual revolution of the renaissance, religious reforms and development of the scientific method;

- those changes enabling the development of ship technology, merchant navies and colonization, originally as a means to wealth and power;
- growing exposure to and demand for imported luxuries, mostly by the aristocracy;
- the development of agricultural methods, freeing agrarian populations from a subsistence lifestyle;
- the development of banking and monetization of the economy;
- increased social mobility and egalitarianism, freeing the poor to adopt elements of the consumption patterns of the rich;
- a growing role for central government and the emergence of the nation state.

These and other developments laid the foundations for the Industrial Revolution, which brought large parts of the European and American population into a world increasingly structured by technology and markets. Economic development since the Industrial Revolution has involved massive changes in consumption patterns that both stimulated and were stimulated by changes in production patterns, technology and culture. These changes are explored in this section.

Economic development

The eighteenth century in Britain saw considerable investment in agricultural development, infrastructure and institutions. Land-holdings were concentrated and improved agricultural techniques adopted. Roads and canals were built. The banking system expanded and paper credits became a normal form of currency. All of these changes, and others, contributed to population growth, and to growing individual wealth, stimulating demand for material consumption. Landes (1969) gives this growth in consumption much of the credit for stimulating the investment and innovation in manufacturing that became the Industrial Revolution.

The efficiency improvements were based initially on institutional changes, in particular the specialization and division of labour in factories, rather than on technological changes. However, with the concentration of production in larger factories, mechanization became possible. Capacity rose rapidly and unit costs fell, stimulating further growth in consumption.

Industrialization took different forms, and proceeded at differing paces, in the leading countries of northwest Europe and America. Britain lost its lead in industrialization to North America in the nineteenth century because of a variety of economic and cultural factors (Landes 1969). One of the most important of these was the willingness of Americans to accept standardized products that could be mass-produced. British producers had not quite lost the sense of being master craftsmen, producing to specification for an aristocratic clientele. France, in contrast, was much slower to industrialize because of an explicit rejection of commercialism.

During the twentieth century the process of specialization and increasing scale has continued. The growing importance of transnational firms and international trade has permitted very narrow specialization through the contracting-out of services and component manufacturing. Just a few firms now dominate economic sectors ranging from the production of aircraft and computer chips to processed foods, banks and hotels.

Twenty-fold increases in labour productivity in Europe, North America and Australasia over the past 200 years have permitted a continuing shift in economic structure, first from agricultural production to industry. In recent decades, the industry share in the economy has declined, giving way to services. Another major feature of the past two centuries has been the growing role of government in the economy.

Technological change

Throughout the past two centuries, productivity increases have been enabled by technological change. Innovation has often been described as the driving force behind economic development. In the eighteenth century, the innovation was mainly in the mode of production. Developments in science and engineering led to numerous innovations in products—including the bicycle, electric lamp, car, and many others—through the nineteenth century. However, it is the twentieth century that has seen the most rapid explosion in the diversity and quantity of consumer products.

Some economic historians, beginning with Kondratieff and Schumpeter, claim to have identified 'long waves' in the economy, associated with cycles of innovation, investment in newly developed clusters of technology, and then stagnation (Freeman & Perez 1988). There have been five such waves in industrialized countries since the Industrial Revolution in Britain, bringing successive phases of technical and economic development.

- Early industrialization occurred first in Britain from the 1770s, and was concentrated in the textile industry and iron-working, with the mechanization of traditional manufacturing industries.
- A second phase of development began, also in Britain, from around 1830, with the introduction of steam engines as an industrial power source, and the beginning of railways. North America rapidly overtook Britain during this 'railroadization' phase.
- The third phase, from around 1880, was led by the USA and Germany; it included electrification and the development of the heavy engineering industry. Mass consumption began to diversify in this phase, as entrepreneurs became increasingly aware of the potential for marketing new products.
- The USA again led the fourth phase, of 'Fordist' mass production and mass motorization, lasting from the late 1930s through to the 1980s.
- A new phase seems to have emerged during the 1990s involving information and communication technologies and other 'high-tech' industries, led by the USA and Japan.

Each of these new phases led to a transformation of infrastructure, production and consumption patterns and lifestyles.

Cultural shifts

The massive technological changes and productivity increases of the past 200 years could not have occurred without large cultural changes. One of the many circumstances supporting the take-off of industrial culture in England and America was the presence of the Protestant 'work ethic'. Work was supposed to be a source of personal identity, purpose and a relationship with God. In the first hundred years of industrialization, most of the population was characterized as 'workers'. However, being an employee in a factory or mine was very different from working as a subsistence farmer or cottage manufacturer. Labourers had to develop habits of working continuously to the clock in a large, hierarchical system. There was considerable anger at the factory system that had reduced textile prices, undercutting the cottage industries and forcing people to accept waged factory work (Landes 1969). Industrialists also faced opposition from factory owners and craftsmen who tried to maintain a more traditional working style. Industrialization entailed a struggle between alternative cultures and world views, from which expansionism emerged as the dominant force.

A new cultural change began to occur in the second half of the nineteenth century, with the development in the USA of the department store, and more generally the proliferation of shops in industrialized countries. With the introduction of public postal services and mail-order companies, access to innovative and cheap goods spread into rural areas. The increasing access to goods previously confined to the rich led to concerns about the escalation of 'conspicuous consumption'. Consumption was described by Thorstein Veblen in 1899 as a status-building activity in which the middle classes emulated the 'leisure class'.

The twentieth century's developments in production patterns were accompanied by the emergence of 'the consumer' as an identity. Henry Ford has been credited with inventing the link between mass production and mass consumerism in the 1920s by setting up schemes to help his workers buy their own cars. However, the emergence of advertising as a profession making use of the new media of radio and television also had a central role. The shift in the description of the general population from 'workers' to 'consumers' occurred mostly after World War II. Whereas those of us with interesting jobs continue to define ourselves by our work, many people increasingly define their identity and communicate it to others through their choice of consumption patterns (Schor 1998). Consumption similarly defines our membership of communities. These links with identity and community make it very difficult for individuals to imagine changes in their consumption patterns.

Changes in attitudes to time have been another fundamental part of the cultural adjustment to industrial society. Mechanical clocks created a new, linear perception of time; the development of the electric light, central heating and air conditioning reduced dependence on daily and seasonal cycles. Time has become a commodity. Many consumer goods have been aimed at 'saving' time. Some are bought to substitute for time—-for example, busy parents buy gifts for their children to make up for spending insufficient time with them. In part, this shift in attitude to time is an extension of the principle of division of labour into our personal lives. We get machines or other people to do our household chores so that we can concentrate on doing the things that we do best and that earn us the most money. In recent years, there has been a further shift in which technology is used to give us more control over our personal schedules. Examples include video recorders, allowing us to shift the time at which we watch TV shows; freezers, allowing us to shift the time at which we go shopping; and electronic communication, allowing us to be in touch wherever we are, whenever we want.

Mechanisms shaping consumption

In the previous section I touched on several mechanisms that help to shape consumption patterns, including:

- demographic, economic and technological change;
- resources, infrastructure and time constraints;
- motivation, habit, need and compulsion;
- social structures, identities, discourse and symbol.

The current section explores these mechanisms in a little more depth.

Demographic, economic and technological change

Population, economic growth and technology are usually represented as independent drivers in the economic models that are used to evaluate policy responses to environmental challenges. This is in fact very misleading: demographics, economic development and technology are interdependent, although the linkages are subject to debate and cannot easily be quantified. On the whole, countries and regions with high population growth in recent years have seen only slow increases—or even reductions—in income per person from a very low level.

Low rates of fertility tend to correlate with more rapid economic and technological development, partly because all three result from higher levels of education, health care and empowerment, especially female empowerment (Gaffin 1998). These are also factors that contribute in low-income countries to the rapid growth in material consumption that most of us would agree is very much needed.

Demographic change is also important in shaping consumption patterns in wealthier countries. Immigration is causing rapid population growth in many rich countries, notably Australia, Canada, New Zealand and the USA. In these circumstances, immigrants tend to adopt the high consumption levels prevalent in their new surroundings, while introducing aspects of their own culture to their new community and contributing to the diversity of tastes. The ageing of wealthy populations, resulting from a combination of low fertility rates and extended life spans, is another factor contributing to consumption growth, especially in areas such as travel, healthcare and other services. Changes in family relationships, closely linked to increased mobility, are resulting in smaller households requiring more material possessions, space, building fabric and vehicles per person.

Economic development has a crucial role in shaping consumption patterns. Many features of modern economies encourage increasing consumption. Among the most important are the ready availability of personal credit and the expectation of ever-rising incomes, which reduce the incentive to save and encourage people to live on future earnings. Material consumption is also boosted by high rates of labour force participation, combined with the increasing monetization of relationships between people and institutions, and by the failure to price environmental and social externalities that makes material products cheap. These circumstances all help to feed what Juliet Schor calls the 'cycle of work and spend', leading people to buy products and services where previously they might have spent more time doing things for themselves or engaging in reciprocal favours with friends and neighbours.

In the environment policy discourse, technological change is usually seen as an alternative to changing behaviour or consumption patterns, but technological change and behaviour are closely linked (Michaelis 1998). Large improvements in 'eco-efficiency' involve changes in products, which only succeed when consumers are prepared to buy them. Advocates of 'eco-innovation' have emphasized the need for governments and firms to place as much emphasis on improving resource efficiency as they have historically placed on improving labour productivity. It might be possible to achieve long-term, continuing improvements in resource efficiency through well-designed policy frameworks, but such strategies might also slow improvements in labour productivity. The oil price increases in 1973/74 and 1979/80 led to rapid energy efficiency improvements in the industries of countries in the Organization for Economic Co-operation and Development, but labour productivity improvements slowed at the same time. Reducing the growth of labour productivity would tend to reduce growth in income per person and hence in levels of consumption.

The physical world: resources, time and infrastructure

The physical world imposes inevitable constraints on consumption patterns. Rapidly expanding individual consumption in the twentieth century, and an emphasis on saving time, can be understood as a response to a world in which natural resources were plentiful but labour (or time) was scarce. It is often argued that we are moving into an era when natural resources might become scarce, and labour more abundant—hence the advocacy for a shift in emphasis from labour productivity to resource productivity. In contrast, current economic development is based on knowledge and creativity more than on labour or resources. The well-educated are seeing rapid income growth and are under constant time pressure because of the demand for their services, while the less-educated see falling wages and are working harder to maintain household income.

Infrastructure is an essential enabling factor for growth in consumption. The techno-economic models mentioned in the previous section were associated with successive waves of infrastructure development. At present, the most rapid development is in communication infrastructure: information, communication and entertainment are expected to be among the strongest areas of consumption growth in coming years.

Engineers and designers have become increasingly aware in the past two decades of the role of infrastructure design in shaping consumption patterns. This is particularly evident in housing and transport. Uncontrolled urban sprawl has been a major contributor to dependence on the car in many cities in industrialized countries. Attention is only now beginning to be paid to redesigning the infrastructure for more sustainable lifestyles, and for many cities this task seems prohibitively expensive.

Globalization and increasing interconnectedness are already contributing to consumption trends. The availability of high-quality communications networks is encouraging the development of highly dispersed communities, which feeds back into escalating demand for transport systems.

Motivation, need, habit and compulsion

Although economic and physical circumstances help to shape consumption, they do not explain why people consume. We can look for motivation and desire first within the individual. Maslow (1954) explained motivation in terms of human needs, which he divided into categories: physiological needs, belongingness, esteem and 'self-actualisation'. He saw these categories as a hierarchy, arguing for example that we are only concerned about self-esteem when we have had enough to eat. This has been largely discredited (Douglas *et al.* 1998) but Maslow's categorization of needs remains useful. Max-Neef (1991) proposed an alternative, much more complex categorization of needs, divided into 'having', 'doing', 'being' and 'relating' needs, and emphasized the distinction between needs and 'satisfiers'. Often we might try to use ineffective satisfiers to meet particular needs—for example, eating or shopping in an attempt to address feelings of loneliness.

Some of our physiological needs require material consumption. In principle, there is no reason why belongingness and esteem should do so. However, as noted in the previous section, in a materialist culture, material goods are part of the way in which we establish our identities and status, express ourselves and obtain membership of social groups. Hence our levels of material consumption far exceed our physiological needs. Veblen criticized 'conspicuous consumption' as a form of social display, a means of competing for status. Many subsequent writers have added to Veblen's analysis, arguing that material consumption has an important and positive role, in meeting our needs for self-definition, self-esteem, communication with others, and identification and positioning within social groups. Others have criticized mass consumption as a vain and pathological attempt to meet needs that are poorly addressed in the modern nation state. The work of writers such as Fromm and Illich suggests that compulsive consumption and addiction might result from a search for meaning in a society that has lost its spiritual direction.

Much mainstream analysis of environmental problems and policy responses is based on the assumption that people make rational choices to meet their needs in an optimal way, based on the available information. This is one of the fundamental axioms of neo-liberal economics and has been widely questioned. Supermarket operators recognize that their customers' purchase decisions are highly context-dependent, and considerable research effort has been devoted to designing store layout and ambience to maximize customer spending. Decision-making often seems to be based on habits or routines, or satisfying a small number of criteria, rather than optimizing a wide range of variables. The form in which people receive information also has a strong influence on the way in which they respond to it. Information from a familiar source, in particular a member of the family or close friend, is likely to be much more influential than information from a government announcement.

Although some consumption choices can respond to perceived needs, much consumption is habitual. The ratchet of rising consumption levels has been widely observed and was noted by Jean-Jacques Rousseau in 1755 (Schor 1998; Wilk 1999). What was once luxury rapidly becomes habit, and then need. This can result partly from a fundamental human tendency towards repetitive behaviour, observed by Freud. It might be partly that we are biologically adapted to prefer the familiar. We might even be adapted to shun lower-quality food and physical surroundings once we have experiences of a higher quality. However, the ratchet of perceived needs also has a social dimension.

Social structure, identity, discourse and symbol

Modern American and European culture emphasizes the individual as a self-contained person with intrinsic motivations. In many other cultures, individuals are mainly understood in relation to others, and behaviour is largely explained in terms of contextual factors (Hofstede 1980). The American/European belief in the autonomous individual might be a dangerous delusion, given the extent to which our motivations and perceived needs are moulded by our social context. In particular, the French sociologist Bourdieu has demonstrated a strong link between taste and social class. Moisander (1998) has shown that consumption patterns are shaped by identity with groups that might define themselves in a variety of different ways. Schor (1998) observes that Americans who watch TV dramas and soap operas for long periods tend to compare their lifestyles with those of the relatively wealthy characters portrayed, leading to an escalation of expectations.

Consumption patterns can also be understood partly as an outcome of social frameworks, power relationships and alliances. Most people will tend to adopt a dominant lifestyle, not because it makes them happy but because it responds to the prevailing interests and conventions in society.

The structure of the social context contributes to individuals' moral ideals and identity, to their areas of empowerment or constraint, and to the options that they perceive to be open to them. Social structures allow some individuals to influence the consumption patterns of others. For example, women often purchase food and clothing for other household members, whereas men are more influential over large household expenditures. Individuals within wider communities also influence each other's consumption patterns and habits in a variety of ways, depending on the social structure and their respective positions within it.

Perhaps the most controversial influences on consumption patterns are those of mass communication. Narrative and symbol carried by the mass media form a large part of the means through which ideas, arguments and values are transferred from the public to the private sphere, and ultimately might be integrated into individuals' consciousness and identity. Moisander (1998) has observed that consumption choices respond strongly to personal morals or ethics. It is in shaping ethics that the public narrative has a particularly strong role.

Advertising is perhaps the most obvious mechanism by which the mass media can influence consumption patterns, although perversely this influence is disputed by the advertising industry. The power of advertising almost certainly does not lie in its ability to persuade people to make rational choices to behave differently but in the frequent repetition of symbols and value statements so that they gradually become integral parts of mainstream culture and thought. Other important cultural media include television and other drama, public debate, popular music, the visual arts and novels.

The linking of symbols to fundamental values might also be important in shaping behaviour. Ger *et al.* (1998) compare the symbolism of consumption patterns, based on interviews and observations, in Denmark, Turkey and Japan. They find, not surprisingly, that the symbolic attractions of resource-intensive consumption patterns are more powerful than those of sustainable consumption patterns. The symbolic attachments are different depending on the country and the subculture within the country.

Alliances between powerful groups can have a dominant role in determining societal norms through both narrative and symbol. Governments, transnational companies, financial institutions, the press and media represented the main power alliance in the late twentieth century. One example of an alliance supporting a specific interest is the 'road lobby'. This coalition of business interests, professions, government departments and citizens' groups played a strong role in the early development of roads and road-based transport. In recent years, the strength of the coalition has made it difficult for alternatives to the car to flourish.

Changing consumption patterns

There is an urgent need for governments and other agents for change to take on a more comprehensive view of the mechanisms shaping consumption patterns. This paper has suggested a few that might be particularly important. This section concludes by identifying some areas in which action could be taken.

Demographics

Demographic change is causing concern for a variety of social reasons, but it must be understood as a symptom rather than a cause. Actions to improve demographic stability are also likely to contribute to making consumption patterns more stable. Relevant actions might include improving educational opportunities, especially for girls, in the poorest regions; developing better healthcare and social services; and a wide variety of policies that contribute to economic development, community empowerment and stability, all of which reduce the incentive for migration.

Economic and institutional frameworks

Many features of the economic framework help to shape consumption patterns. There is a need to rethink the relative incentives to save and spend. Further examination is needed of the social costs of using personal credit to stimulate consumption. New indicators are needed to replace gross domestic product and consumer spending as indicators of economic well-being. One alternative that has been widely discussed is the development of concepts of natural and social capital (in addition to financial capital) as key economic indicators. There is also a need to address the relative pricing of human time and skills, information, and natural resources. Many institutional and individual writers have advocated the reform of subsidies to polluting and resource-intensive activities, and the introduction of environmental charges or taxes. However, such taxes are controversial. Their introduction might depend on better environmental education and better community participation in decision-making.

Technological innovation

Technological innovation is widely viewed as an important part of a strategy for sustainability. However, policy thinking in this area is usually narrowly focused on R&D spending, and picking and subsidizing certain technologies. The design of national systems for innovation has tended to be guided more by the aim of maximizing national competitiveness rather than sustainability. A much more coherent, strategic approach is needed to stimulate and guide innovation in the direction of a more sustainable techno-economic system. R&D incentives should be coordinated with subsidy and tax reforms and support for niche markets. More international cooperation is needed to share both the costs and the results of experimentation. There is also a need for social innovation to be supported alongside and as a part of technological innovation.

Infrastructure

Given the current rapid development of communication networks, a considerable effort is warranted to avoid some of the mistakes experienced in past waves of infrastructure development. More research is needed to understand how communication networks currently influence consumption, and how this influence might evolve in the future. Efforts are also needed to ensure that conventional transport and urban infrastructures support more sustainable lifestyles. This includes shifting the balance of road provision from private cars to non-motorized transport, reducing parking provision in cities, working with communities to make city centres more attractive, and encouraging mixed use so that people are able to live, work and socialize within the same neighbourhood.

Narrative and symbol

The role of narrative and symbol is consistently underplayed in policy analysis, perhaps partly because this area is one in which politicians are the experts rather than the policy analysts. More research is needed to improve understanding of the influence of public discourse and symbol on personal behaviour. Many forms of art, expression and communication help to shape culture. Producers of TV drama, musicians, politicians and advertisers need to be enrolled in the effort to improve the status and attraction of sustainable lifestyles.

Shifting alliances

Power networks are also underplayed by policy analysts, again perhaps because they are the stuff of politics. Again, more research would help to clarify the linkages between governments, industries, science and technology, the press, media and other agents, and to understand how they shape and influence consumption patterns. Efforts are needed by partners in these alliances to let in other stakeholders and to begin to develop a culture that embraces change rather than the status quo.

References

Douglas, M., Gasper, D., Ney, S. & Thompson, M. 1998 Human needs and wants. In *Human choice and climate change*, vol. 1 (*The societal framework*) (eds S. Rayner & E.L. Malone), pp. 195–263. Columbus, Ohio: Battelle Press.

Freeman, C. & Perez, C. 1988 Structural crises of adjustment: business cycles and investment behaviour. In *Technical change and economic theory* (eds G. Dosi, C. Freeman, R. Nelson, G. Silverberg & L. Soete), pp. 38–66.

Gaffin, S.R. 1998 World population projections for greenhouse gas emission scenarios. In *Mitigation and adaptation strategies for global change*, vol. 3, nos 2–4, pp. 133–170. Dordrecht, Boston and London: Kluwer Academic Publishers.

Ger, G., Wilhite, H., Halkier, B., Laessoe, J., Godskesen, M. and Røpke, I. 1998 Symbolic meanings of high and low impact daily consumption practices in different cultures. Working paper prepared for Second European Science Foundation Workshop on Consumption, Everyday Life and Sustainability, Lancaster University, UK. See http://www. lancs.ac.uk/users/scistud/esf/title.htm

Hofstede, G. 1980 *Culture's consequences: International differences in work-related values*. Beverley Hills: Sage.

Landes, D.S. 1969 *The unbound Prometheus: technological change and industrial development in Western Europe from 1750 to the present*. Cambridge University Press.

Maslow, A. 1954 *Motivation and personality*. New York: Harper & Row.

Max-Neef, M. 1991 *Human scale development—conception, application and further reflection*. London: Apex Press.

Michaelis, L.A. 1998 Economic and technological development in climate scenarios. In *Mitigation and adaptation strategies for global change*, vol. 3, nos 2–4, pp. 231–261. Dordrecht, Boston and London: Kluwer Academic Publishers.

Moisander, J. 1998 Motivation for ecologically oriented consumer behaviour. Working paper prepared for Second European Science Foundation Workshop on Consumption, Everyday Life and Sustainability, Lancaster University, UK. See http://www.lancs.ac.uk/users/scistud/esf/title.htm

Schor, J. 1998 *The overspent American*. New York: Basic Books.

Wilk, R. 1999 Towards a useful multigenic theory of consumption. Paper presented at the Summer School of the European Council for an Energy Efficient Economy, Mandelieu, France.

Can affluent people adapt to a world of sustainable development?

Patrick Bateson

The Provost's Lodge, King's College, Cambridge CB2 1ST, UK

Introduction

The idea that I wish to explore in this paper is the extent to which humans might be able to limit willingly their use of resources—which in some parts of the world has become profligate. It might be argued for example that, in the main, humans are too conservative and too selfish to give up what makes their lives easier and, they imagine, happier. It is depressing to observe the steady drift towards obesity in the industrialized world and the extreme reluctance of most people who have cars to use public transport even when it is manifestly cheaper and more convenient. If the unwillingness to change is constrained by human psychology, we need to understand those constraints as a matter of some urgency. Part of the problem could be that human behaviour was adapted to circumstances in which people no longer live. I believe that this possibility has some substance which should be recognized. Another part of the problem is that habits, once formed in an individual's development, are not easily changed. On the optimistic side, however, humans are able to change their behaviour—even when psychological mechanisms, designed in the course of evolution, might seem to dictate otherwise. Indeed, I shall argue that other equally well-adapted mechanisms facilitate such change. The ideas in this chapter are discussed at greater length in Bateson & Martin (1999).

Well-designed behaviour

'Biology is the study of complicated things that give the appearance of having been designed for a purpose', wrote Richard Dawkins (1986) in *The blind watchmaker*. Dawkins took the image of the watchmaker from an argument developed by William Paley in the early nineteenth century. 'It is the suitableness of these parts to one another; first, in the succession and order in which they act; and, secondly, with a view to the effect finally produced', wrote Paley about the reaction of someone who contemplates the construction of a well-designed object. Paley, who became a bishop, regarded the design that he saw everywhere in Nature as proof of the existence of God. These days, few biologists would try to pin their religious faith on biological evidence, and the design to which Paley referred would be attributed instead to the evolutionary mechanism that Charles Darwin called natural selection.

Darwin's theory of evolution by natural selection is universally accepted among scientists, even if arguments continue over the details. Darwin proposed a three-stage cycle that starts with random variation in the form and behaviour of individuals. In any given set of environmental conditions some individuals are better able to survive and reproduce than others because of their distinctive characteristics. The historical process of becoming adapted notches forward a step if the factors that gave rise to those distinctive characteristics are inherited in the course of reproduction. Suppose, for example, that an individual bacterium happens to have heritable characteristics that make it resistant to the latest antibiotic. Whereas all the others are killed by antibiotics, this one will survive and multiply rapidly. Before long, the world (or, at least, the hospital ward) is full of antibiotic-resistant bacteria. Darwinian evolution requires no unconscious motives for propagation, let alone conscious ones.

The proposition that living organisms' bodies, brains and behaviour were adapted over the course of evolution to the conditions in which they lived is at least familiar to most non-biologists. An adaptation is a modification that makes the organism better suited to survive and reproduce in a particular environment—-better suited, that is, than if it lacked the crucial feature. The perception that behaviour is designed springs from the relations between the behaviour, the circumstances in which it is expressed and the resulting consequences. The closeness of the perceived match between the tool and the job for which it is required is relative. In human design, the best that one person can do will be exceeded by somebody with superior technology. If you were on a picnic with a bottle of wine but no corkscrew, one of your companions might use a strong stick to push the cork into the bottle. If you had never seen this done before, you might be impressed by the selection of a rigid tool small enough to get inside the neck of the bottle. The tool would be an adaptation of a kind. Tools that are better adapted to the job of removing corks from wine bottles are available, of course, and an astonishing array of devices have been invented. One ingenious solution involved a pump and a hollow needle with a hole near the pointed end; the needle was pushed through the cork and air was pumped into the bottle, forcing the cork out. Sometimes, however, the bottle exploded and this tool quickly became extinct. As with human tools, what is perceived as good biological design might be superseded by an even better design, or the same solution might be achieved in different ways.

Biologists have been properly warned not to write evolutionary accounts in which the past is seen as leading purposefully towards the goal of the present blissful state of perfection. A clear distinction is necessarily and wisely drawn between the present-day utility (or function) of a biological process, structure or behaviour pattern, and its historical, evolutionary origins. Darwin noted, for example, that although the bony plates of the mammalian skull allow the young mammal an easier passage through the mother's birth canal, these same plates are also present in the mammals' egg-laying reptilian ancestors. Their original biological function clearly must have been different from their current function (Gould & Vrba 1982).

For animals, the ultimate arbiter of priority in organizing their own behaviour is reproductive success, and the consequences are sometimes astonishing—at least when judged from a human perspective. The male emperor penguin brooding his mate's egg over the Antarctic winter cannot be relieved by his mate because the growth of the ice shelf puts the sea and food beyond reach. So, in the interests of producing an offspring, he fasts for months—a feat that any human would find impossible. Other potential solutions to this problem, such as shorter stints of brooding and trekking repeatedly across the ice shelf during the winter, were presumably less efficient. The penguins that fasted all winter were the ones that had the best design. Examples like this emphasize how dependent is the organization of behaviour on the ecology of the species. A corollary is that the particular way in which a given system develops will also depend on ecology.

The evolutionary process does not require a simple correspondence between genes and adaptive behaviour. Darwinian evolution operates on individuals that have developed within a particular set of conditions. If those conditions are stable for many generations, the changes that matter will be primarily genetic. Individuals vary; some survive and reproduce more successfully than others because they possess a crucial characteristic; and close relatives are more likely to share that characteristic than unrelated individuals. Apparent design is produced, even when it is at the end of the long and complicated process of development. However, the environment does not cease to be important for evolution just because it remains constant. Change the environment and the outcome of an individual's development might be utterly different. Indeed, if an individual does not inherit its parents' environment along with their genes, it might not be well adapted to the conditions in which it now finds itself.

It is, alas, all too obvious that humans do stupid things that run counter to their best interests. John Bowlby (1969), who pioneered a biological approach to behavioural development, was well aware that some adaptations that benefited humans in the past have become dysfunctional in the radically different modern world. Behaviour such as seeking out and receiving pleasure from eating sweet or fatty foods was doubtless vital in a subsistence environment, but in a well-fed society it does more harm than good. This is where issues of sustainability intersect with the seemingly intractable aspects of human behaviour.

Unconscious choice

Humans like to think of themselves as being in command of their destinies. Indeed, the presumption of law, morality and, indeed, common sense would be that they are right. But even legal systems, not famous for recognizing grey areas, accept pleas of diminished responsibility in criminal trials. Modern evidence suggests that much of what we do is unconscious or, at least, preconscious.

People can choose a course of action without knowing why or reflecting on what they do. It just seemed right at the time. Those who wish others to buy their wares or use their services seek to manipulate choice. Supermarkets tempt customers to buy things that they did not know they wanted by skilful arrangements of displays or by wafting the aroma of freshly baked bread through the ventilation system. As people become familiar with certain commercial brands through repeated exposure to advertisements, they will prefer to buy them—mainly because they are familiar. For instance, foreign words made familiar to students by printing them on T-shirts were preferred by the students over foreign words that they had not seen before. Similar effects are obtained in controlled laboratory conditions by using Chinese ideographs (Murphy *et al.* 1995).

Patients with particular sorts of damage to the pre-frontal cortex of the brain provide living proof that rational thought and conscious analysis are insufficient to function well in the real world. Their ability to make even apparently straightforward decisions— especially decisions involving social or personal subtleties—is severely impaired, despite their normal performance in almost any test of intelligence, memory or reasoning. They remain engaged in a trivial activity, neglecting the important activities of daily life. The neurologist Antonio Damasio (1994) described eloquently in his book *Descartes' error: emotion, reason, and the human brain* how these patients seem to lack the biasing that the emotions normally provide when making decisions about budgeting time. Elliot was one such patient who had had a tumour removed from the critical brain area. He returned to work after recovering from the surgery but would not stick to any schedule set for him. When sorting documents he would spend a whole day reading one letter. He lost his job and by degrees his whole life fell apart. Damasio argued that the emotions are crucial in everyday life. He and his colleagues also showed the value of hunches in a gambling task designed to simulate real-life decision-making. Volunteers could win or lose facsimile money by choosing cards from various decks. Unknown to them, choosing cards from 'bad' decks led to overall losses, whereas 'good' decks produced overall gains. After they had experienced some losses, normal people began to choose cards from the 'good' decks before they had consciously realized which strategy worked best. After further experience they became consciously aware of the difference between the good and the bad decks of cards and ceased to play on the basis of hunch (Bechara *et al.* 1997). This study indicated how non-conscious biases advantageously guide behaviour before conscious knowledge or rational analysis comes into play.

Inchoate preferences guide and facilitate conscious evaluation and reasoning. What sets these biases, providing the basis for a well-adjusted emotional life and thence rational decision-making? Much remains unknown, but evidence grows for the biasing effects of certain experience. Like buildings, bodies are difficult to alter fundamentally once they are fully constructed. Such constraints generate continuities in behaviour as well as physical structures. Moreover, people tend to settle into familiar habits and thereby restrict further opportunity for change. However, these properties of human behaviour do not mean that we are incapable of change.

The capacity for change

William James, the elder brother of Henry James and an eminent nineteenth-century psychologist and philosopher, relished the capacity for change. In 1902 he wrote, 'The greatest discovery of my generation is that human beings can change their lives by altering attitudes of mind.' Viewed historically, humans have shown remarkable capacity for rapid change. The transformation of man-made environments, and subsequent human adaptations to them, have been abrupt and recent, relative to human evolutionary history. The earliest forms of civilization, in the shape of systematic farming, emerged less than 10 000 years ago. The first written records appeared 6000 years ago in Mesopotamia and China, and the wheel was invented not long afterwards. Industrialized societies started to emerge within the past 200 years and computers became ubiquitous in the later part of the twentieth century. The changes in environmental conditions from those in which humans evolved have been radical and have occurred when genetic change has probably been negligible.

Contrasting properties of resistance to change and changeability—of elasticity and plasticity—are often found within the same material object. Stretch a metal spring a little and it will return to its former shape. Stretch it too far, however, and it will permanently take on a new shape. Adult humans, too, exhibit plasticity as well as elasticity in their behaviour, their values and their personalities: they remain recognizably the same individual in a variety of situations, yet retain the capacity to change. Compare the robustness of most people in response to life's buffetings with the way in which some individuals profoundly modify their behaviour and attitudes. Continuity and change are not incompatible. The brains that generate behaviour do not consist of springs, of course, but the general property of getting back on track when circumstances allow coexists with an ability to alter direction.

The potential to change and to carry on changing later in life is clearly important, and especially so when the effects of early experience on someone's development have been disruptive or have damaged their psychological well-being. However, once someone becomes set into a particular pattern, is it really possible to wipe the slate? Sigmund Freud followed a long intellectual tradition in emphasizing the formative effects of early experience. A reconciliation between the view that early experience is important and the view that nothing is irreversible was explicit in Freud's psychoanalytical theory. His approach, which was unusual at the time, reflected his belief that seemingly irreversible influences from childhood could be overcome in adults. This view was central to Freud's method of therapy for those whose lives had been damaged by their early experience. Nowadays the idea is widely accepted and is implicit in the vast self-help industry, which is built on the supposition that people can change themselves. Indeed, the pendulum has swung so far that it often seems as though people should be able to change their behaviour and personality as readily as they change their hairstyle.

The earlier, and perhaps excessive, emphasis on early experience might have been rejected because of its implied pessimism that once someone has missed the developmental train, nothing could be done to help them thereafter. The grounds for optimism are in fact considerable, and evidence for sensitive periods early in development can be readily reconciled with evidence for subsequent changes in behaviour. This is seen most clearly when the experience that could cause the change is not normally encountered in later life. An unwillingness to eat novel food means that people will not encounter the flavours and textures that might change their preferences. However, it is not just a matter of preference. The mechanisms in the brain that protect behaviour from change can, under rather special conditions, be stripped away and plasticity is once again possible.

Political and religious leaders of various stripes have throughout the centuries sought to change people's values, and they have sometimes succeeded. How have they gone about it? Instances of what is colloquially called 'brainwashing' can be found, for instance, in the Christian revivalist conversions in eighteenth-century America. During a religious crusade in Massachusetts in the 1730s, the theologian Jonathan Edwards discovered that he could make his 'sinners' break down and submit completely to his will. He achieved this by threatening them with Hell and thereby inducing acute fear, apprehension and guilt. Edwards, like many other preachers before and after him, whipped up the emotions of his congregation to a fever-pitch of anger, fear, excitement and nervous tension, before exposing them to the new ideas and beliefs that he wanted them to absorb. To this day, live rattlesnakes are passed around some congregations in the southern parts of the USA; the fear and anxiety that they induce can impair judgement and make the candidates for conversion more suggestible. Once this state of mental plasticity has been created, the preacher starts to replace their existing patterns of thought. And constant fear is, of course, a hallmark of totalitarian regimes in which dissenting individuals live under the unremitting threat of detention, torture or execution.

The British psychiatrist William Sargant, working in the middle of the twentieth century, was deeply interested in these mind-moulding techniques, and noticed the importance of high emotion in the process of religious conversion. In his book *Battle for the mind*, he drew on a wide range of human experience, including that of military brainwashing (Sargant 1957). He extended his inquiry to the beneficial uses of stress in psychotherapy. In World War II, Sargant helped soldiers suffering from battle fatigue. As part of the therapy, he and his colleagues would deliberately arouse strong emotions in their patients, about events that had no direct connection with the trauma they had experienced. If Sargant was right about the benefits of the emotional experience, then that method has something in common with the psychological technique of 'flooding', in which someone suffering from a phobia is deliberately made frightened in the presence of the object or situation towards which they are phobic—-for instance, by placing a large spider onto the chest of the patient who is terrified of spiders. Contrary to what intuition might suggest, the patient's phobia can be greatly reduced (Rowe & Craske 1998).

It is common practice around the world for army recruits to be treated brutally in the early stages of their training. The individual is broken down through physical and mental pressure before being rebuilt in the form required by the military. The recruits are verbally abused, made to perform pointless menial tasks, forced onto long marches carrying heavy equipment and then by degrees their platoon becomes their family. Away from armies, other methods for inducing psychological plasticity include social isolation, fasting, lowering blood glucose with insulin, physical discomfort, chronic fatigue and the use of disturbing lighting and sound effects.

The so-called Stockholm syndrome, also known as 'terror bonding' or 'trauma bonding', might be yet another instance of psychological plasticity induced by emotional trauma. The term takes its name from an incident in Stockholm in the 1970s, in which a woman who was taken hostage in a Stockholm bank following an unsuccessful robbery formed a strong and long-lasting emotional bond with her captor. She even remained faithful to him during his subsequent imprisonment. Her strange reaction was not unique. Many other victims of violent hostage-taking have ended up siding with their captors against the authorities who were trying to rescue them. Being taken hostage is obviously a traumatic experience, and the hostage-takers might be equally frightened because their lives are on the line as well. In such circumstances, where hostage and captor are exposed to each other while both are emotionally highly aroused, a strong emotional bond can form, bizarrely uniting them against the world outside. As with the various military, political, religious and therapeutic techniques for changing the way in which adults think and behave, the crucial element is the combination of psychological stress and suggestion.

The concept of extreme fear or emotional arousal inducing plasticity helps to make sense of many diverse examples of behavioural change. What might be the neurobiological mechanisms underlying this effect? How does trauma make someone susceptible to fundamental changes in their thoughts and values? What might be the biological link between psychological stress and the processes of plasticity and change in the nervous system?

High levels of psychological stress are associated, among other things, with the rapid synthesis and turnover of the neurotransmitter substance noradrenaline. This chemical messenger of the nervous system has been implicated as an enabling factor in making the adult brain become plastic again. Noradrenaline (known in the USA as norepinephrine) is released in the mammalian brain, at the endings of neurons throughout the body, and from the adrenal glands just above the kidneys. It is released in response to psychological stress, among other things; in humans, a mildly stressful situation such as giving a public speech will typically elicit a 50% rise in the amount of noradrenaline circulating in the bloodstream (Martin 1997).

An experiment on the visual system of cats gave some valuable insights into the connection between noradrenaline and plasticity. The mammalian visual system is normally changeable only during an early stage in the individual's life. The capacity of an eye to stimulate neurons in the visual cortex of the cat's brain depends on whether that eye received visual input between about one month and three months after birth. If one eye is deprived of visual stimuli during this period, it virtually loses its capacity to excite cortical neurons thereafter, no matter how much visual stimulation it receives. The eye consequently becomes functionally blind, even though it remains physically unimpaired. Once the dominance of the other eye is established, it is exceedingly difficult to change the relationship with the unused eye. Similarly, binocular vision cannot easily be disrupted in individuals reared normally once it has become established. However, infusing noradrenaline into one hemisphere of the visual cortex of older cats can re-establish plasticity and enable further change to occur in response to visual experience. If animals reared normally are deprived of the use of one eye during the period of noradrenaline infusion, binocular control of the neurons is lost in the visual cortex of the hemisphere that was infused. No such change occurs in the visual cortex of the other hemisphere. In other words, noradrenaline can reverse in adulthood what would otherwise be unchangeable (Pettigrew & Kasamutsu 1978).

The ability to manipulate the brain chemically, and thereby permit renewed change in adulthood, is striking. It would nevertheless be simplistic to suppose that noradrenaline alone is responsible for making neuronal connections responsive to new sensory inputs. The parts of the cat's visual cortex in which renewed plasticity occurs are also connected to neurons emanating from many other parts of the brain that might also have a role. The enabling condition for renewed change could be a particular cocktail of neurotransmitters rather than the presence of just one.

The sheer variety and complexity of behaviour and its underlying psychological systems inevitably means that any sweeping statement about the possibility of change must eventually come unstuck. The self-help industries that promise relief from shyness, depression, sloth, overeating, or addiction to nicotine deliver results only some of the time. Once developed, some patterns of behaving are strongly buffered against subsequent change. Preferences for certain types of food and for particular places tend not to change. They might be stable for good design reasons, because change can be disruptive and costly. However, not to change can, in certain circumstances, carry an even bigger cost, which perhaps explains why behavioural characteristics tend to become plastic under conditions of stress.

The deterministic character of modern biology seems to subvert the commonsense view that individuals can make free choices. If it were supposed that humans were designed to respond like robots to the imperatives of survival and reproduction, then what is to be said about choice, freedom of will and personal responsibility? An obvious answer is that a well-designed brain should respond to the consequences of behaviour; if an understanding of the likely consequences can be achieved without actually performing the act, then a person who knows that they will be rewarded or punished for certain acts is bound to be influenced by that knowledge. A brain designed in that way invites the evolution of societies with explicit social approval of certain activities and explicit disapproval of others. The rules for what is or is not acceptable might be arbitrary, but only fools and the brave will ignore them. The point is that people do make sensible, well-planned decisions. A proper understanding of biology embraces free will.

Conclusion

Opportunism must always have had an important role in driving historical change. As in a large restaurant, many different dishes are being cooked at the same time in the kitchen of behavioural development. Occasionally the behavioural dishes are thrown together and something quite novel—and useful—is produced by chance. Humans are perfectly capable of appreciating the value of their own experiments, and the emerging effects have had an extraordinary influence on human history. The combination of spoken language, which has obvious utility in its own right, and manual dexterity in fashioning tools, which also has obvious utility, combined at a particular and relatively recent moment in evolutionary history to generate written language. The discovery of written language took place several times and in several forms in different parts of the world, with ideas represented by pictures or spoken sounds represented by symbols. Once invented, the techniques were quickly copied and became crucial elements of modern civilization. It was that active combining of different capacities that started the whole remarkable cultural sequence of events.

The evolutionary approach to psychology does not imply that individuals do not make free choices. Individuals clearly do make a big difference to what happens in their lives through their choices and decisions. They can be surprised by the consequences of their own action. A well-designed brain should be able to anticipate the consequences of various courses of action and choose between them on the basis of their likely costs and benefits.

Planning before doing is clearly of great advantage. It is obvious that people often do make sensible, well-considered decisions. Their decisions might reflect developmental mechanisms that are themselves the results of evolutionary processes, but it would be foolish to look for adaptation in every individual choice. A proper understanding of biology brings back free will—even if the freedom is constrained and sometimes used unwisely.

The conditions in which change happens might sometimes involve stress, but the capacity to change in adulthood is nevertheless real. For those who are old, the rediscovery that they can still change bears out the point that development continues until death. Modern biology does not support common prejudices about the inability of humans to change. Aggression and violence, for example, are depressingly widespread and frequently gratuitous. However, they are also mutable, as are the human institutions of war that harness them. Despite the shameful catalogue of wars and violence that have darkened human history, civilization and society are demonstrably capable of creating conditions in which the great majority of people behave peaceably towards their fellow humans for long periods. It is crucial to have a good understanding of those conditions when we contemplate the undoubted need that those who live in great affluence change the way in which they behave so as to create a sustainable world.

References

Bateson, P. & Martin, P. 1999 *Design for a life: how behaviour develops*. London: Cape.
Bechara, A., Damasio, H., Tranel, D. & Damasio, A.R. 1997 Deciding advantageously before knowing the advantageous strategy. *Science* **275**, 1293–1295.
Bowlby, J. 1969 *Attachment and loss*, vol, 1 (*Attachment*). London: Hogarth Press.
Damasio, A.R. 1994 *Descartes' error: emotion, reason, and the human brain*. New York: Grosset/Putnam.
Dawkins, R. 1986 *The blind watchmaker*. London: Longman.
Gould, S.J. & Vrba, E. 1982 Exaptation—-a missing term in the science of form. *Palaeobiology* **8**, 4–15.
Martin, P. 1997 *The sickening mind: brain, behaviour, immunity and disease*. London: Harper Collins.
Murphy, S.T., Zajonc, R.B. & Monahan, J.L. 1995 Additivity of nonconscious affect—combined effects of priming and exposure. *J. Person. Soc. Psychol.* **69**, 589–602.
Pettigrew, J.D. & Kasamutsu, T. 1978 Local perfusion of noradrenaline maintains visual cortical plasticity. *Nature* **271**, 761–763.
Rowe, M.K. & Craske, M.G. 1998 Effects of varied-stimulus exposure training on fear reduction and return of fear. *Behavioral Research Therapy* **36**, 719–734.
Sargant, W. 1957 *Battle for the mind*. London: Heinemann.

The social implications of consumption

Andrew Jordan and Tim O'Riordan

Centre for Social and Economic Research on the Global Environment, School of Environmental Sciences, University of East Anglia, Norwich, Norfolk NR4 7TJ, UK

Introduction

Consumption is a social act as much as it is an economic one. Consumption bestows identity, self-perspective, status and the admiration of peers. For sustainable consumption to gain hold, sustainability as an ideal will have to be universally valued in society, and in the image of social responsibility. Unless and until consuming sustainably achieves the same moral and social status as consuming unsustainably, any government-led policy to achieve sustainable consumption will be hard pressed to achieve significant results. The more basic problem faced by any government wishing to re-steer consumption is that the basic driving forces reside within the structure and organization of an increasingly globalized consuming culture. This culture in turn is so deeply embedded within the operation of the world economy that it is unlikely to be radically changed by *ad hoc* policy interventions. Making consumption sustainable is a task of the utmost complexity. It demands government policies that are focused, committed and enduring.

Consumption is promoted in part by the commodification of wants and by the advertising business, which in 1998 spent more than $413 billion worldwide (which equates to about 1% of total global economic output) (Brown *et al.* 1999). Elkington (1998) reports that young adults in Europe are exposed to around 20 000 television commercials each year. Consumption might not produce happiness, but it does produce the drive for self-expression in a society in which 'lifestyle' and 'image' are promoted by the media and by socially transmitted signals of approval and disapproval. Needs and wants are not as clearly separable as many would have us believe: both are the product of social conformity and individual belongingness. This point is forcefully made by Douglas *et al.* (1998), who conclude that human needs and wants are not separable, that there is an interconnection between material needs and social bonding, and that cultural and social connections are the main controller of consumption. Hence, what governments and trading regimes might search for in the drive towards more sustainable consumption might actually have little relevance for the individual and the household.

Consumption is also a vital component of a modern, global economy. The consumer purse is the engine of jobs and innovation. Within the process of consumption, however, standards of environmental care and social responsiveness do appear. Consumers are increasingly alive to the needs to market products that are not environmentally damaging or socially disruptive in the life cycle from source through consumption to disposal. An intermediate stage to sustainable consumption, therefore, is product stewardship and producer responsibility, in which goods and services are specifically created to minimize environmental burdens. However, a more serious set of political, moral and ethical problems loom if the goal of policy is to lower overall consumption per person. This can result in more unsustainable outcomes for the poor and vulnerable than its specific contribution to sustainability overall. Sustainable consumption will have to accommodate a variety of objectives and expectations, few of which have been adequately articulated or examined by politicians.

Sustainable consumption as an interlinked goal

Sustainable consumption is a necessary but insufficient condition for achieving sustainable development. Sustainable development requires a complicated and ever recalibrated balance to be struck between economic, environmental and social goals. As it is currently being interpreted in current policy debates (see Agenda 21, Chapter 4; Organization for Economic Co-operation and Development 1997; von Weizsacker *et al.* 1997), the concept of sustainable consumption directly addresses the first two of these objectives but greatly neglects the third. This chapter seeks to explore the social implications of trying to make consumption more environmentally and economically sustainable. We therefore try to be integrationist and synthesizing for this volume as a whole, rather than just being an 'add-on' to some of the more focused contributions. We specifically highlight the politically problematic question of intra-generational fairness as well as the more explicitly acknowledged goal of improving inter-generational equity. This means being sure to take fully into account the consequences for those already disadvantaged as a result of any significant shift to sustainable consumption, as well as the well-being of future citizens, bearing in mind that their values might not be the same as ours.

The argument that consumption overall in Europe should be reduced (as distinct from re-steered) has been an important strand in the North–South population–consumption debate (Grubb *et al.* 1993, pp. 30–33; Johnson 1993; Jordan & Voisey 1998). From an 'ecocentric' or 'ecologist' perspective (for details see O'Riordan (1976) and Dobson (1990)), reducing consumption is a *sine qua non* of sustainable development—a totemic ideal to be aspired to. Jonathon Porritt, a leading British environmental thinker, has argued, '[i]f you want one simple contrast between green and conventional politics, it is our belief that quantitative demand must be reduced, not expanded' (Porritt 1986, p. 136). The so-called 'deep' green position on consumption holds that excessive consumption pushes Society up against ecological limits and of itself is incapable of fulfilling deeper (i.e. more spiritual) human needs and aspirations. Nowadays, the green movement makes less explicit reference to this radical line of critique but it still has its exponents (Frank 1999). Today, reducing consumption by some kind of politically inspired intervention or price control is widely regarded as being wholly infeasible by most conventionally minded politicians and is condemned outright as moral dictatorship in some quarters. If this final comment seems slightly exaggerated, recall the last-ditch efforts made by the US Government in 1992 to alter the section of Agenda 21 (paragraphs 4.3–4.5) addressing the triangular relationship between environmental degradation, consumption in the North and poverty in the South (Johnson 1993, pp. 151–152). For a large proportion of the world's population, unbridled consumer choice is an unquestioned assumption of the capitalist system.

At present, the furthest that most governments seem prepared to go down this road in terms of the 'modification of demand' (UK Department of the Environment (DOE) 1995, p. 13), is in reducing 'the environmental impacts associated with the production and consumption of goods and services which meet human needs' (UK Department of Environment, Transport and the Regions (DETR) 1998, para. 2). The implicit assumption is that individuals rather than governments are best placed to make this most 'political' of choices—what counts as a human 'need' and what is a more frivolous social 'want' (Dobson 1990, pp. 89–102). Douglas *et al.* (1998, p. 201) argue that 'wants and needs do not come from inside the person, nor are they ordered according to private preference…. Social life is a continuous negotiation of acceptable demands.' Owens (1997) argues powerfully that the 'demand imperative'—satisfying some predicted level of future human demand for natural resources—is deeply embedded in the economic and political structure of industrialized societies, to the extent that it is widely portrayed in the dominant discourses of policy as an important measure of their vitality and health. Consequently, the current debate about consumption in modern Western societies is framed in terms of how to redirect consumption, and how to ensure that any given product or service actually enhances social, environmental and economic well-being as a linked aim (Robins & Roberts 1998). Only then is society likely to identify the 'win–win–win options' needed to achieve sustainable development (UK Round Table on Sustainable Development 1999, p. 22). For any other interpretation to be socially tolerable, the values of society will have to shift most fundamentally towards sustainability.

The social implications of consumption

Fashionable policy concepts such as Integrated Product Policy (i.e. the idea that resource consumption and pollution need to be reduced at every stage in a product's lifecycle from its initial design through to its use and final disposal), Factor 4/10 and product stewardship, are primarily directed at improving the overall level of resource productivity—that is, the efficiency with which natural resources (including energy) are used and disposed of (see Environmental Data Services (ENDS) 1997; Hawken *et al.* 1999; Myers (this volume); von Weizsacker *et al.* 1997; UK House of Commons Environment Committee 1999). This topic has been given much attention in reports on eco-efficiency (see, for example, Carley & Spapens 1998). However, the fact remains that new technology will emerge only if there are guiding processes in policies with levies, or in regulation via long-term agreements. Eco-efficiency cannot be guaranteed out of current pricing and regulatory arrangements.

Significantly, the debates around these concepts are usually much less concerned with the important social dimension of consumption. Sometimes social and environmental objectives are complementary—for example, improving public transport reduces congestion, relieves pollution and combats social exclusion by extending access to those who are currently unable to own their own private vehicle—but often they are not. Any change in private access to the motor vehicle carries with it important implications for the mobility of those already disadvantaged by limited access to transport, namely the poor, the disabled and the distant. Sustainable consumption is about finding a better reconciliation of these different factors.

The most important social aspects of the sustainable consumption debate and the questions that they trigger in relation to the development of future policy are therefore those described under the following headings.

The international politics of consumption

Since the 1970s, consumption has been linked to population growth as part of a highly politicized but ultimately unproductive debate between North and South. If we consider the likely social implications of consumption in the North, then new and largely unconsidered questions come to the fore, for example: is the implementation of Factor 4 in the North a necessary or a sufficient condition for worldwide sustainability? Or are other things required of the North to enable developing countries to leapfrog to sustainability such as 'fairer' systems of trade? And in any case, might the introduction of Factor 4 in the North lead to economic and social disruption in resource-dependent and exporting southern countries? Indeed, should developing countries begin their 'new development' on Factor 4 lines? And if so, who should pay for that? This is a particularly thorny issue in the debate on climate change. For example, a recent report produced for the World Wildlife Fund by the Tellus Institute estimates that an aggressive policy to curb greenhouse gas emissions could save the USA $43 billion per annum and create 870 000 new jobs by 2010 (World Wildlife Fund 1999). Studies such are these are aimed at allaying the fears of the consuming public in the rich, affluent parts of the world where environmental protection is perceived as a threat to jobs and economic growth. However, what needs to be added to these calculations is an explicit estimation of the likely spillover effects of such cuts on countries overseas, especially those in the developing world.

The social impacts of de-materialization

Improving resource productivity and reducing the consumption of environmentally unsound products will have a profound impact on those whose livelihoods are tied to unsustainable consumption. Coal miners, fish workers and car workers are obvious candidates. How might their changing well-being interests be accounted for in eco-concepts such as Factor 4, Factor 10 and ecological footprints? There is, as the British Government's Panel on Sustainable Development has pointed out, an urgent need for all parts of governments to consider the interlinked social, economic and environmental implications before introducing new policies and new tools on the grounds of promoting 'sustainability' (British Government Panel on Sustainable Development 1999, p. 11).

The social impacts of consumption

There is evidence to suggest that the poor are often disproportionately affected by the by-products of consumption such as air and water pollution, and urban degradation (Been 1994; Cutter 1995; Lewis 1996; Friends of the Earth, UK (FoE) 1999). They are less able to protect themselves from these ill effects (i.e. involuntary social exclusion), whereas the rich do have the means to insulate themselves to a large extent (i.e. voluntary social exclusion) (Voisey & Hewett 1999). The bias in siting unpopular technologies and other locally unwanted land uses ('LULUs') such as nuclear wastes, incinerators and airports near to those who do not have the political mobilization to protest is part of the emerging eco-justice movement in the USA and elsewhere (Blowers & Leroy 1994). Social exclusion reduces social cohesiveness and exacerbates intra-generational inequity. Consumption is a social behaviour that grants esteem and identity to many people: to deny future consumption on politically unaccepted 'sustainability' grounds can have very adverse consequences for disadvantaged peoples unless there is a very careful programme of inclusion in a future society.

The ethical dimension of sustainability

Judging by the commercial success of 'ethical' businesses such as the Body Shop and Café Direct, consumers are deeply concerned about the impact of their purchasing decisions on animals, indigenous peoples and workers, particularly when they are children. MORI polls suggest that a small core of consumers are powerfully influenced by ethical matters, with a further 20% being attentive to this theme. That is a sizeable element of consumer power. Politicians are wary of treading into this politically sensitive and ethically loaded territory of policy-making. Despite the undoubted importance of the ethical dimension in achieving sustainable development, the British Government (UK Department of Environment, Transport and the Regions (DETR) 1998, Box 1) concedes that the underlying issues are 'complex and, at this stage, less well defined than the environmental issues associated with the production and consumption' (i.e. 'greening' growth).

How might these strictly 'non'-environmental impacts be brought into consideration? A growing number of companies, such as Shell, BP, BT and ICI, are recognizing that their businesses have a 'triple bottom line' (social, economic and environmental), and are adapting their reporting and business plans accordingly. A number of firms are currently involved in a pilot project, supported by the United Nations Environment Programme and the European Union, which aims at developing benchmarks and performance criteria, backed up by verifiable reporting requirements (http://www.ceres.org). Companies such as Shell, the Body Shop and the Co-operative Bank have already produced their own social or 'ethical' audits, which combines financial reporting with an account of its impact on key stakeholders including employees, customers, local communities, and present and future generations. The key challenge for the future lies in developing a set of criteria to ensure that these reporting processes are broadly comparable, externally verifiable, and influential on the wider societal implications of changing consumption habits. Currently this is still not happening. Part of the problem has to do with the consumer movement itself, which finds itself on a double-edged sword with regard to the issue of sustainable consumption. On the one hand it fights for environmental quality and fair trade, but on the other the primary focus of its work is on delivering to Western consumers good, cheap consumer products at affordable prices.

Addressing basic human needs

By definition, development is sustainable when it satisfies current needs. Therefore, to what extent do current patterns of consumption in Europe satisfy the basic needs of its citizens? Can, and indeed should, those needs be defined scientifically? We have already suggested that to a large extent, needs and wants cannot be untangled except, perhaps, for the very poorest in society. The 1998 *Human development report* (United Nations Development Programme 1998, p. 51) suggests that 1.5 million families in the UK could not afford an adequate diet in 1994. A recent study by the Joseph Rowntree Foundation (Voisey & Hewett 1999) found that 30% of children in Britain are poor, and that this is a growing proportion. These figures raise difficult questions for any policy of sustainable consumption. For example, to what extent are people prevented from consuming more sustainably by their social circumstances? How do factors such as income and education affect purchasing decisions? What are the causes of 'under consumption' (Acheson 1998) and how can it be addressed sustainably? By the same token, 'overconsumption' leads to obesity, ill health and, in many cases, unhappiness. Policies to encourage sustainable consumption therefore extend far more widely than the environment, touching on issues of health, poverty and education.

Managing the demand for goods and services

Demand management is recognized, though not always explicitly acknowledged, as an integral aspect of the policy debate about sustainable consumption. The British Government has, for example, openly stated that 'the pursuit of more sustainable forms of consumption, including reduced levels of demand and encouraging demand for alternative goods and services … is an important aspect of Government policy' (UK Department of the Environment (DOE) 1997, para. 62). However, managing demand in areas such as transport, energy, water and food raises extremely difficult ethical and moral issues that powerfully challenge the very sovereignty and 'democracy' of consumer choice. How should the political process determine what is necessary and what is unnecessary in consumption matters without breaching basic democratic principles? Should the market be the final arbiter or is some morally imposed regulation required?

The driving forces of unsustainable consumption

In the foreword to the 1998 Human Development Report (United Nations Development Programme 1998, p. iii), James Gustav Speth argues that human society is on a 'runaway consumption train'. It is politically incorrect to implicate advertising and marketing in excessive and wasteful consumption, but their role cannot be ignored in any serious discussion of sustainable development. What is the role of status, identity and social communication in supporting existing consumption patterns? What is the role of consumption in exacerbating social exclusion? There are a variety of reasons why the poor find it hard to behave more sustainably (lack of funds to purchase energy efficiency equipment; inability to afford environmentally friendly products, which are often pitched at the young and the more affluent in society). Furthermore, as Myers and Kent (1998) have detailed, most goods and services are subsidized to varying degrees. There is no 'market' as such, and much consumption is fuelled by prices that distort their true social and environmental costs.

Conclusions

These are the social issues that need to be factored into political decision-making for the sustainability transition. The more basic decisions that both drive and reflect the broader process of societal consumption are, of course, likely to be at the level of the individual consumer. Achieving more sustainable forms of consumption requires the decision-maker to have a clear understanding of the likely environmental, economic and social impacts of his or decision, the likely alternatives, and some sense of overall societal acceptance. Some progress can be made through adjusting the prices, through informational devices such as eco-labels, corporate reports and government information campaigns, and by eco-efficiency technologies. The key point, however, is that sustainability requires 'win–win–win' decisions, which balance environmental quality with social equity and economic development. For that to happen, societal values will need to change.

References

Acheson, D. 1998 *Independent inquiry into the inequalities of health*. London: HMSO.
Been, V. 1994 Locally undesirable land-uses in minority neighbourhoods. *Yale Law Journal* **103**.
Blowers, A. & Leroy, P. 1994 Power, politics and environmental inequality. *Environmental Politics* 3, 197–228.
Brown, L.R., Renner, M. & Halweil, B. 1999 *Vital signs 1999*. New York: Norton.
British Government Panel on Sustainable Development 1999 *Fifth report*. London: Department of Environment, Transport and the Regions.
Carley, M. & Spapens, M. 1998 *Sharing the world: sustainable living and global equity in the 21st century*. London: Earthscan.
Cutter, S. 1995 Race, class and environmental justice. *Progress in Human Geography* **19** (1), 111–122.
Dobson, A. 1990 *Green political thought*. London: Harper Collins.
Douglas, M. *et al.* 1998 Human needs and wants. In *Human choice and climate change* (ed. S. Rayner & E. Malone), pp. 259–261. Columbus, Ohio: Battelle Press.
Elkington, J. 1998 *Cannibals with forks*. London: Capstone.
Environmental Data Services (ENDS) 1997 *Eco-efficiency: building a government strategy*. ENDS Report 272, pp. 20–24.
Friends of the Earth, UK (FoE) 1999 http://www.foe.co.uk/pollution-injustice/
Frank, R.H. 1999 *Luxury fever: why money fails to satisfy in an era of excess*. New York: Free Press.
Grubb, M., Koch, M., Munsen, A., Sullivan, F. & Thomson, K. 1993 *The Earth Summit agreements*. London: Earthscan.
Hawken, P., Lovins, A.B. & Lovins, L.H. 1999 *Natural capitalism: the next industrial revolution*. London: Earthscan.

Johnson, S. 1993 *The Earth Summit*. London: Graham & Trotman.

Jordan, A. & Voisey, H. 1998 The 'Rio process': the politics and substantive outcomes of 'Earth Summit II'. *Global Environmental Change* **8** (2), 93–97.

Lewis, D. 1996 *Not just a pretty place*. Birmingham: Groundwork Trust.

Myers, N. & Kent, J. 1998 *Perverse subsidies: tax $s undercutting our economies and environments alike*. Winnipeg: International Institute for Sustainable Development.

Organization for Economic Co-operation and Development (OECD) 1997 *Sustainable consumption and production*. Paris: OECD.

O'Riordan, T. 1976 *Environmentalism*. London: Pion.

Owens, S. 1997 Negotiated environments? Needs, demands, and values in the age of sustainability. *Environment and Planning* A **29**, 571–580.

Porritt, J. 1986 *Seeing green*. Oxford: Blackwell.

Robins, N. & Roberts, S. 1998 *Consumption in a sustainable world*. Oslo: Norwegian Ministry of the Environment.

UK Department of the Environment (DOE) 1995 *Government response to the House of Lords Select Committee on Sustainable Development*. London: HMSO.

UK Department of the Environment (DOE) 1997 *Five years on from Rio: UK position paper*. London: Department of the Environment.

UK Department of Environment, Transport and the Regions (DETR) 1998 *Consumer products and the environment*. London: DETR.

UK House of Commons Environment Committee 1999 *Reducing the environmental impact of consumer goods* (11th Report. Session 1998–1999). London: HMSO.

UK Round Table on Sustainable Development 1999 *Fourth annual report* (March 1999). London: Department of Environment, Transport and the Regions.

United Nations Development Programme 1998 *Human development report 1998*. Oxford University Press.

Voisey, H. & Hewett, C. 1999 *Reconciling social and environmental concerns*. York: Joseph Rowntree Foundation.

von Weizsacker, E., Lovins, A.B. & Lovins, L.H. 1997 *Factor four: doubling wealth, halving resource use*. London: Earthscan.

World Wildlife Fund 1999 *America's global warming solutions*. Washington, DC: The Tellus Institute for World Wildlife Fund.

Carrying capacity, overshoot and the need to curb human consumption

Mathis Wackernagel

Redefining Progress, One Kearny Street, 4th Floor, San Francisco, California 94108, USA

The illusion of self-sufficiency

People's lives depend on the biosphere. The thin layer of living systems covering planet Earth provides a steady supply of the basic requirements for life. It also makes industrial processes possible because it provides energy for heat and mobility, wood for housing and paper products, and water for cleansing. In addition, people need good-quality food and uncontaminated drinking water for healthy living.

Through photosynthesis, green plants convert sunlight, CO_2, nutrients and water into plant matter, and all the food chains that support animal life—including our own—are based on this plant matter. Nature also absorbs our waste products and provides life-support services such as climate stability and protection from ultraviolet radiation. If we are to continue to have good living conditions, we must ensure that Nature's productivity is not used more quickly than it can be renewed, and that waste is not discharged more quickly than Nature can absorb it. In other words, humanity needs to stay within the ecological capacity of the biosphere.

Although this dependence is obvious once we trace the metabolism of our lives, it is also obscured by our daily lives. An endless number of obfuscation mechanisms operate at every level of society. Respected academic traditions perpetuate the idea of Nature as a 'purely social construction'. Consumer advertising presents images of never-ending abundance, which it portrays as a human right. City departments whisk waste into landfills and sewers, and utilities provide electricity with rarely a black-out and clean water at any rate demanded. Road space for cars is free. Retail shelves brim over, no matter how much we buy. The supply of such goods has been so smooth that its delivery is taken for granted. Meanwhile, technology promises the invention of new resources, and the dominant global cultures offer aggressive economic expansion, personal and otherwise, as the only model of success.

In other words, our inability to deal with ecological limits is not determined by insufficient understanding of the natural science of sustainability. Solid analysis and documentation of the challenges is undoubtedly a necessary condition for meaningful action. However, the principal stumbling blocks for dealing creatively, effectively, and humanely with limits are shaped by significant socio-psychological characteristics of our dominant culture. These perceptual stumbling blocks require more attention if we are to learn to live in ways that are compatible with Nature's limited capacity to regenerate itself. This means that science's most effective contributions to the sustainable consumption conundrum are likely to come not only from technical and natural science laboratories but also from practical insights of pedagogy, social psychology, and systems thinking.

This goes beyond an abstract reflection on which world view we ought to subscribe to and how we choose to perceive the world. There are some non-negotiable boundary conditions; the question is how we should organize ourselves best within these constraints. I call them 'non-negotiable' because it is easy to prove the social constructivists of Nature wrong. We need only to invite them to hold their breath for 10 minutes, or to stop eating for two months. Those who see resources as an invention of the human brain are invited to prepare for a travel through empty space and build their life-support systems out of ideas only, taking nothing from the biosphere or the earth's crust. The challenge, however, is to provide constructive and practical ways to bring human actions in line with the necessity to reduce human impact. This is not a mandate for deprivation: human beings can learn to pursue the best possible quality of life within the means of Nature.

Carrying capacity, ecological limits, and overshoot: why we can exceed ecological capacity

Generally, biologists define the carrying capacity of a given species as the maximum population number that can be sustained by a given habitat (e.g. the biosphere) without systematically deteriorating the integrity and productivity of its ecosystems (Rees 1990; Miller 1996, p. 169). If sustainability means quality of life for all, within the capacity of the biosphere, the concept of carrying capacity reminds us of an ultimate rule of sustainability: build the best possible quality of life for all, but do not transgress the regenerative capacity of the biosphere.

The problem is that humanity can quite easily transgress ecological limits. Ecologists call this 'overshooting carrying capacity' (Catton 1980; Meadows *et al.* 1972). Overshooting means that natural capital is depleted more rapidly than it regenerates. In consequence, the biocapacity for future generations is reduced and the risk of ecosystem collapse is increased. The fear is not primarily the possibility of human extinction; rather, such collapses could mean tremendous hardship for a large number of people.

In the past, the discussion of limits focused more on the availability of non-renewable resources, such as minerals, ores, and fossil fuel, because they are essential ingredients of industrial processes (Meadows *et al.* 1992). However, it has become evident that living (or biotic) resources are even more at peril. Life support services are being eroded that not only supply economic resources but also maintain cycles and functions necessary to keep the planet liveable (Daily 1997). These include water cycles, protection from ultraviolet radiation by the stratospheric ozone layer, natural pollination services, genetic continuity, climatic stability, and the absorption of biological wastes. These services are undermined by overharvesting and waste overload. The use of non-renewable resources has itself become a significant force in threatening ecological functions in so far as the wastes that they produce threaten these life functions. Examples are the accumulation of CO_2, the build-up of waste, contamination caused by the release of human-made compounds and materials from the earth's crust, and urbanization of the most fertile land.

In fact, 'the most fearsome environmental damage', summarizes the author Bill McKibben, 'comes from things going as they're supposed to go, just at much too high a level' (McKibben 1998, p. 112). In other words, it is the cumulative effect of all these seemingly insignificant resource uses and waste releases that in their entirety put a load on the biosphere that is exceeding its regenerative capacity. Renewable resource use and waste production do not grow asymptotically or logistically towards the accessible carrying capacity, as many models assume. This can occur because assimilative capacities do not immediately restrict waste production, and harvests of renewable resources do not become increasingly hard as sustainable yield limits are exceeded. Because there is no immediate feedback from the ecosystems, only systematic (or at least indicative) resource accounting that compares sustainable harvests with actual harvests, as done in forestry and fisheries management, can inform resource administrators about the state of their natural capital asset. The consequence of not acting upon such accounting information has been painfully experienced in many areas of the world, a vivid case being the collapse of the Atlantic cod fishery (Harris 1998).

Measuring carrying capacity: historic limitations and breakthroughs

The question is: How can one track human use of Nature in an accounting framework? This task is easier for most other animals. For them, population size is a good indicator of carrying capacity. It is a robust measure, because the way in which they exploit ecosystems is almost entirely determined by their biology, as is the amount that they consume. Even when diseases or territorial behaviour affect their population density, the biology of these control mechanisms changes little over time. However, there are significant differences between the human species and most other animal species. People have:

- inflicted systematic changes on ecosystems in the past (e.g. land use change from forests to arable land, drainage of wetlands, irrigation, terracing);
- influenced Nature's productivity through a variety of management approaches (some types of exploitation can actually increase Nature's productivity);
- unlinked their consumption from their biological or metabolic needs, creating orders of magnitude of difference between possible levels of consumption per person; and
- accessed Nature's resources and services from distant places, which makes it possible to overcome regional carrying capacity constraints.

Hence the question of how many people the earth (and even more so a given country) can support becomes impossible to answer in any meaningful way. Changing assumptions about living standards and technology produce varying and seemingly contradictory answers. Cohen's (1995) overview of carrying capacity studies over the past 100 years testifies to that. Some interpret the range of answers for carrying capacity as a proof for the uncertainty of ecological limits.

The way out of this impasse is to reframe the question. Focusing on 'maximum human load' shifts the issue from the number of people that can be sustained to the question of how much human load the biosphere can tolerate. There are several advantages to this formulation. It allows one to disentangle the many intertwined aspects of the population-environment conundrum. One can separate the biological question about the biosphere's regenerative capacity from the social and technological questions about how the human load is adding up and who occupies which share. Human load is a direct function of population numbers, the level of people's consumption and the eco-efficiency of production, all of which can be subjected to clear-cut empirical studies. Furthermore, the issue of risk can be addressed by looking at how close the aggregate human load should grow to the maximum regenerative capacity of the biosphere to maintain its long-term biological stability. Obviously, regenerative capacity cannot be determined with absolute precision. However, it is possible to develop estimates of upper limits, as many studies comparing human load with regenerative capacity have done (Vitousek *et al.* 1986; Buitenkamp *et al.* 1992; Wackernagel *et al.* 1999). (Many studies agree that if people should have the opportunity to live at the material level of average Western European residents, the biosphere might only be able to sustain 2 billion people (Pimentel *et al.* 1999; Willey 1999).)

This turns the original question on its head. It becomes not how many people can live from a given ecological capacity, but how much capacity is necessary to support existing people with their particular consumption pattern. In other words, one needs to measure how much carrying capacity a given population appropriates. Showing who takes how much of what is available points to the core issues of the sustainability challenge: the scale question (how big is the economy in comparison with the biosphere's regenerative capacity) and the distributional question (who gets what, at whose cost?).

Comparing human consumption with ecological capacity: the ecological footprint

The 'ecological footprint' concept is designed to answer the question of how much ecological capacity there is in comparison with how much people use (Wackernagel & Rees 1996). In this way, the ecological footprint is a measure for obtaining a first approximation of human use of natural capital. It documents how much biologically productive space is necessary for a given population to produce the resources that it consumes and to absorb the corresponding waste that it generates, with the use of prevailing technology. In other words, it reflects the natural capital necessary to maintain the current material throughput of economies, under current management and production practices. It is an accounting tool that records what is currently happening, not what could happen in the future (it should therefore not be mistaken for a predictive model, although it does provide a baseline from which to construct such models).

Our latest estimates, based on readily available United Nations statistics, are presented in Table 1. They show the amount of biocapacity currently used by the average citizens of 52 nations. For example, the average Canadian required over 6 ha of biologically productive land and 1 ha of ecologically productive sea space to provide for his or her 1995 level of consumption (Wackernagel *et al.* 1999). These add up to 7.2 ha or 72 000 m² (720 times 100 m) or more than ten typical soccer fields. In comparison, the average American lives on a footprint about 30% larger, the average Italian on about half the size. The average Swiss and the average German occupy a little under 5 ha. Because we assume optimistic yield figures for our calculations and do not (yet) include all uses of Nature, these figures underestimate the biologically productive areas truly necessary to sustain these people. (Estimates of the waste side are poorly represented in our current footprint accounts. One reason is that amounts of waste, and even more so their ecological impacts, are poorly documented in international statistics. The United Nations Development Program (1998) claims in its Human Development Report that agricultural losses due to air pollution are $4.7 billion for Germany, $2.7 billion for Poland, $1.8 billion for Italy and $1.5 billion for Sweden.)

By comparison, how much is available? The globe's spherical surface contains 51 Gha. One-quarter of it is biologically productive, which means that it is covered by plant life. Most of it is on the land. The other three-quarters is not lifeless but is far sparser in ecological activities. Offshore ocean, Antarctica and the Sahara desert fall into this category. Dividing all the biologically productive land and sea on this planet by the number of people inhabiting it results in a statistical average of 2.1 ha per person in 2000. This is less than half of what is necessary to accommodate the footprint of an average Swiss citizen. Of this 2.1 ha per person, 1.6 ha is land-based natural and managed ecosystems such as

Table 1. The ecological footprints of nations

(For 52 countries, representing 80% of the world population, this table lists its 1995 population, its ecological footprint, available bio-capacity and national ecological surplus (deficit where negative) for 1995; three on a per-person basis and the last two in national absolutes. The results are calculated for 1995, and all areas are expressed in bioproductive area with world-average yields. This means that areas with higher productivity seem proportionally larger in these accounts. Table and calculation adapted from Wackernagel *et al.* (1999).)

	population in 1995	nation's average ecological footprint/(ha per person)	nation's available bio-capacity/(ha per person)	nation's ecological surplus/(ha per person)	total eco-footprint of nation/km²	total available bio-capacity of nation/km²
Argentina	34 768 000	3.0	4.4	1.4	1 060 000	1 542 000
Australia	17 862 000	9.4	12.9	3.5	1 672 000	2 305 000
Austria	8 045 000	4.6	4.1	−0.5	373 000	332 000
Bangladesh	118 229 000	0.6	0.2	−0.3	659 000	275 000
Belgium	10 535 000	5.1	1.7	−3.4	535 000	174 000
Brazil	159 015 000	3.6	9.1	5.6	5 670 000	14 545 000
Canada	29 402 000	7.2	12.3	5.1	2 122 000	3 615 000
Chile	14 210 000	2.3	2.6	0.3	329 000	372 000
China	1 220 224 000	1.4	0.6	−0.8	17 311 000	7 323 000
Colombia	35 814 000	2.3	4.9	2.6	828 000	1 765 000
Costa Rica	3 424 000	2.8	2.0	−0.8	96 000	68 000
Czech Rep	10 263 000	3.9	2.6	−1.4	405 000	263 000
Denmark	5 223 000	5.9	4.2	−1.7	309 000	221 000
Egypt	62 096 000	1.4	0.5	−1.0	896 000	294 000
Ethiopia	56 404 000	0.7	0.5	−0.2	389 000	274 000
Finland	5 107 000	5.8	9.9	4.1	298 000	506 000
France	58 104 000	5.3	3.7	−1.6	3 062 000	2 153 000
Germany	81 594 000	4.6	1.9	−2.8	3 788 000	1 540 000
Greece	10 454 000	4.2	1.6	−2.6	438 000	165 000
Hong Kong	6 123 000	6.1	0.0	−6.1	375 000	2 400
Hungary	10 454 000	3.1	2.6	−0.5	322 000	269 000
Iceland	269 000	5.0	6.8	1.9	13 000	18 000
India	929 005 000	1.0	0.5	−0.5	9 353 000	4 472 000
Indonesia	197 460 000	1.3	2.6	1.4	2 509 000	5 199 000
Ireland	3 546 000	5.6	6.0	0.4	197 000	213 000
Israel	5 525 000	3.5	0.3	−3.1	191 000	17 000
Italy	57 204 000	4.2	1.5	−2.8	2 414 000	837 000
Japan	125 068 000	4.2	0.7	−3.5	5 252 000	873 000
Jordan	4 215 000	1.6	0.2	−1.4	69 000	8 200
Korea, Rep.	44 909 000	3.7	0.4	−3.2	1 649 000	199 000
Malaysia	20 140 000	3.2	4.3	1.1	642 000	872 000
Mexico	91 145 000	2.5	1.3	−1.3	2 306 000	1 158 000
Netherlands	15 482 000	5.6	1.5	−4.1	867 000	238 000
New Zealand	3 561 000	6.5	15.9	9.4	230 000	565 000
Nigeria	111 721 000	1.0	0.6	−0.4	1 069 000	656 000
Norway	4 332 000	5.5	5.4	−0.1	237 000	234 000
Pakistan	136 257 000	0.9	0.4	−0.5	1 278 000	552 000
Peru	23 532 000	1.4	7.5	6.1	341 000	1 766 000
Philippines	67 839 000	1.4	0.8	−0.7	965 000	523 000
Poland, Rep.	38 557 000	3.9	2.0	−1.9	1 511 000	786 000
Portugal	9 815 000	3.8	1.8	−2.0	368 000	172 000
Russian Fedn	148 460 000	4.6	4.3	−0.4	6 839 000	6 314 000
Singapore	3 327 000	6.6	0.0	−6.5	219 000	1 000
South Africa	41 465 000	3.0	1.0	−1.9	1 224 000	415 000
Spain	39 627 000	3.8	1.4	−2.5	1 524 000	553 000
Sweden	8 788 000	6.1	7.9	1.8	534 000	695 000
Switzerland	7 166 000	4.6	1.8	−2.9	333 000	127 000
Thailand	58 242 000	1.9	1.3	−0.7	1 120 000	740 000
Turkey	60 838 000	2.1	1.2	−0.8	1 260 000	756 000
UK	58 301 000	4.6	1.5	−3.0	2 667 000	903 000
USA	267 115 000	9.6	5.5	−4.1	25 532 000	14 697 000
Venezuela	21 844 000	4.0	4.7	0.7	869 000	1 018 000
World	**5 687 114 000**	**2.2**	**1.9**	**−0.3**	**126 080 000**	**110 091 000**

forests, pastures and arable land, and 0.5 ha is ecologically productive ocean areas, most of which are located on continental shelves.

However, there is a slight complication. Because the human species shares this planet with over 10 million other species, it needs to share some of the planet's space with them. Today, many human uses of Nature exclude other species. For example, agriculture calls any species that is not exploitable a 'weed', and much of the most fertile land has been paved over for urbanization. Conservation biologists point out that the protection of biodiversity might require significant portions of the biologically productive land. To make sure that we understate ecological scarcity and avoid exaggerating the severity of the ecological challenge, we are using the politically courageous but ecologically insufficient (today, *ca.* 3% of the biologically productive space is set aside worldwide as protected parks, but conservation biologists believe that far more might be required merely for the utilitarian goal of biodiversity preservation (Noss & Cooperrider 1994)) suggestion made in the Brundtland Report *Our common future* (World Commission on Environment and Development 1987), which invites the world community to protect 12% of the biologically productive space for biodiversity. (Proposals similar to those in the Brundtland Report have been put forward by the World Wide Fund for Nature's (WWF) Living Planet 2000 Campaign, launched in 1996, and much earlier by IUCN/World Conservation Union (1980) in their World Conservation Strategy.) Using this far too conservative number, the available bio-productive space per person shrinks from 2.1 to 1.8 ha per person. With the predicted global population of 9 billion for the year 2050 or before (for the most recent population estimates of the United Nations, visit www.popin.org/longrange/tab2.htm.), the available space will be reduced to 1.2 ha per person, including the bioproductive sea space.

Already, the average Italian uses more than double what is available for the average world citizen, or nearly three times more than is at hand per Italian within their national territory. Worldwide, however, humanity's footprint might exceed the eco-capacity of the biosphere by one-quarter—and if we put aside that meagre 12% for the other species, the overshoot is 15%. In other words, humanity consumes more than Nature can regenerate and is eating up the globe's natural capital stock. From this point of view the challenge of sustainability lies in answering the question **how can all people enjoy satisfying lives within an average of no more than 1.8 ha per person?** This is the most significant question we are faced with in research, business and politics.

This 2 ha represents only the minimum requirement for ecological sustainability. Clearly, footprint sizes reveal little or nothing about people's quality of life or well-being, which need to be measured separately. In addition, footprints account for only the potentially renewable parts of people's use of Nature. Those aspects that are systematically at odds with ecological integrity such as the release of heavy metals, radioactive substances or cumulative toxins are not even included. Even so, the ecological footprint provides a useful quantitative approximation of the extent to which human demands are, or are not, within the means of Nature. In addition, it can document who is occupying which portion of the biosphere's services.

For example, our distributional analyses show that 70% of the world's population have an ecological footprint smaller than the world's per person ecological capacity (2.1 ha). These 70% only occupy one-quarter of humanity's total footprint (Wackernagel & Bolibaugh 1999). With an overshoot of 20% (i.e. a global footprint exceeding the biospheric capacity by 20%), one-quarter of the human footprint that these 70% claim translates into an equivalent of one-third of the global carrying capacity. In comparison, this 70% of humanity appropriates about the same capacity as the 4% of the human population with the largest footprints. These are people with a footprint larger than 10 ha per person. As a comparison, 9.6 ha per person is the average footprint of Americans. According to our estimates, 9% of the UK is in this '10+' category, 37% of the Americans, 5% of the Italians, 5% of Mexicans, 6% of Chileans and 32% of Australians (Wackernagel & Bolibaugh 1999).

The effects of technological advances, declining resource prices and the possibilities of trade

Some argue that future markets and technology will react in time to ecological constraints. Declining resource prices are an indication for them that these mechanisms are indeed already operating. However, I would argue that most of the prevailing technology and the expanded trade regimes make it possible for societies to increase their ecological throughput. In fact, many technological advances have locked industrial society into resource-intensive infrastructure traps such as car-dependent city designs, making it harder for people to choose less resource-intensive lifestyles.

Because there is only delayed feedback from overshoot, this flow of energy and resources through the human economy is expanding far beyond local (and global) biocapacities. Better financing schemes, more cheaply convertible currencies, faster money transfers, fewer trade taxes, more reliable international legal frameworks, better communication networks, more potent transport capacity, and more efficient resource extraction all help to access the remaining resources at a faster rate with less human effort. This expedites not only society's resource throughput but also its capacity to amplify its technological capacities for exploiting resources.

Today, these technological enhancements allow humanity to access, ever more quickly and easily, the more remote resource stocks, which have been exploited to a smaller extent. In consequence, resource exploitation over past decades has become easier more quickly than humanity's demands for these resources increases. The result is a decline in resource prices and a global market insensitive to present scarcity and physical limitations. This explains the current situation in which market scarcity and ecological scarcity are increasingly separate phenomena, the former representing the immediate supply on the market (as expressed in its market price), the latter giving an indication of total existing stocks (as expressed in biophysical accounts).

As global trade unlinks market scarcity from ecological scarcity, the healthy and necessary feedback loop between ecological capacities and human consumption is broken, allowing modern society to lead the dangerous life of an ecological invader. These invaders, as one can learn from well-documented cases in biology and ecology, at first enter new niches and consume everything that they can get hold of. Eventually, however, once the niches' capacities are lost through overexploitation, the population and its consumption collapses to significantly lower levels. The difference between yeast in a sugar-rich environment or rabbits released for the first time in Australia (both prototype situations of ecological invasion) and human beings is merely that people have the intellectual capacity to foresee their potential demise.

Most people find such a collapse unacceptable. We deny that such collapses can happen, as is illustrated by all UN population scenarios. Further, we fool ourselves by believing in continued economic growth, despite the evidence that it has become more an act of aggression against other people and species than a means of improving lives. For some time this might be possible as a result of the increased accessibility of Siberia, the further exploitation of the Amazon basin, and the fact that Canada's forests can still be clear-cut. In the case of these regional forests, extending the harvest rate causes a timber glut on the global market. What actually is resource use beyond sustainable yields seems to buyers as an overabundance of resources. With these short-term strategies, humanity is only buying time but unfortunately wasting it by entrenching the conventional self-destructive path. The outcome of such 'invasive' behaviour should not come as a surprise. Even higher levels of consumption will be reached before collapse, once the last ecological niches have been pillaged.

Boulding (1971) summarized this counterproductive behavior in 'Dismal Theorem', which essentially states that if the only ultimate check on growth is ecological misery, then the human economy will grow until the situation is sufficiently miserable that it cannot expand any more (Bartlett 1997). If this theorem is true, technological advances to help to overcome ecological constraints will provide space for further expansion and, sooner or later, increase the total sum of misery. Only by constraining human expansionism with humane obstacles can the 'Dismal Theorem' be proved untrue.

Conclusion: how much consumption curbing may be necessary?

If we accept the fact that we are currently in overshoot and assume that current use of Nature indeed exceeds its regenerative capacity by one-quarter, it might be a wise idea to reduce society's overall impact by a modest 1% per year. If humanity is lucky, such a slow reduction might be sufficient to secure a functional and productive natural capital stock one or two generations from now, at a time when people can live once again within the Earth's carrying capacity.

What would such a reduction mean if at the same time the annual rate of population growth persisted at 1.6%? Let us suppose for this calculation that the reduction in resource consumption should be primarily the responsibility of the richest 20% receiving 84% of the world income; at the same time, let us assume that the other 80% of humanity would stay at their current consumption levels (bearing in mind that many of them need to consume more to lead healthy lives). Consequently, this richest segment of humanity would need to reduce its resource throughput by 6% every year. This reduction is more rapid than the Kyoto Protocol proposes for CO_2 reduction. Most industrial countries promised to cut their CO_2 emissions by 8% in a time span of 10–15 years. Moving out of overshoot, however, would require a reduction of this amount every year. A daunting task, indeed.

However, the challenge of reducing our load on Nature is not just a simple mechanical proposition of slashing consumption by whatever means necessary: such a strategy would be both inhumane and unsuccessful. It must be done as a balancing act between biocapacity and the human pursuit of the best possible quality of life. On the one hand, there is no doubt that people strive to have fulfilling and secure lives; and it is obvious that this endeavour has a material dimension. Indeed, industrial societies are characterized by encouraging resource and waste intensive lives. On the other hand, we can see the results of this expansion. Humanity's drain on Nature has grown by many orders of magnitude over past centuries and is now reaching the point of ecological overshoot. This ecological strain is accompanied by a social one because, more than ever, people's demands on Nature are unequal. In fact, their resource use also varies by orders of magnitude.

Recent decades have been marked by reaching limits, with overall resource demands and waste production exceeding the regenerative capacity of the biosphere. This overshoot can only be maintained temporarily. The question is therefore how to secure an acceptable quality of life in the future. Some people will need more; others will defend vigorously their level of material consumption. Further, there will be more people. Hence, securing the quality of life for all within the means of Nature will be the toughest and most fundamental challenge that people in the North and South will have to face in the decades to come. Curbing human consumption might be unpopular but it is necessary if a systematic destruction of our life-support systems is to be avoided. Advocates of sustainability are often popularly perceived as holding in contempt the human quest for the best possible quality of life, but true respect for this most legitimate of human desires dictates that we find ways of pursuing it within the means of Nature.

References

Bartlett, A. 1997 Reflections on sustainability, population growth, and the environment—revised. *Renewable Resources Journal*, winter 1997–1998.

Buitenkamp, M., Venner, H. & Wams, T. (eds) 1992 *Action plan sustainable Netherlands*. Amsterdam: Dutch Friends of the Earth.

Catton, W., Jr., 1980. *Overshoot: The ecological basis of revolutionary change*: Urbana: University of Illinois Press.

Cohen, J.E. 1995 *How many people can the Earth support?* New York: Norton.

Daily, G. (ed.) 1997 *Nature's services: societal dependence on natural ecosystems*. Washington, DC: Island Press.

Harris, M. 1998 *Lament for the ocean: the collapse of the Atlantic cod fishery, a true crime story*. Toronto: McClelland & Stewart.

IUCN/World Conservation Union 1980 *World Conservation Strategy: living resource conservation for sustainable development*. Gland, Switzerland: IUCN, UNEP, WWF.

McKibben, W. 1998 *Maybe one: a personal and environmental argument for the single child family*. New York: Simon & Schuster.

Meadows, D.H., Meadows, D.L. & Rander, J. 1992. *Beyond the limits*. Toronto: McClelland & Stewart Inc.

Meadows, D.H., Meadows, D.L., Randers, J. & Behrens III, W. 1972. *The limits to growth*. New York: Universe Books.

Miller, T. 1996 *Living in the environment: principles, connections, and solutions*. Belmont, California: Wadsworth.

Noss, R.F. & Cooperrider, A.Y. 1994 *Saving nature's legacy—protecting and restoring biodiversity*. Washington, DC: Island Press.

Pimentel, D., Bailey, O., Kim, P., Mullaney, E., Calabrese, J., Walman, L., Nelson, F. & Yao, X. 1999 Will limits of the Earth's resources control human numbers? *Environment, Development, and Sustainability* **1**, 19–39.

Rees, W.E. 1990 The ecology of sustainable development. *The Ecologist* **20** (1), 18–23.

United Nations Development Program (UNDP) 1998 *Human development report 1998*. Oxford University Press.

Vitousek, P.M., Ehrlich, P.R., Ehrlich, A.H. & Matson, P.A. 1986 Human appropriation of the products of photosynthesis. *BioScience* **34** (6), 368–373.

Wackernagel, M. & Bolibaugh, C. 1999 *Worldwide distribution of footprints and purchasing power*. San Francisco: Redefining Progress.

Wackernagel, M. & Rees, W.E. 1996 *Our ecological footprint: reducing human impact on the Earth*. Gabriola Island: New Society Publishers.

Wackernagel, M., Onisto, L., Bello, P., Linares, A.C., Falfán, I.S.L., García, J.M., Guerrero, A.I.S. & Guerrero, M.G.S. 1999 National natural capital accounting with the ecological footprint concept. *Ecological Economics* **29** (3), 375–390.

World Commission on Environment and Development (WCED) 1987 *Our common future*. Oxford University Press.

Willey, D. 1999 *Optimum world population*. Optimum Population Trust Brief 99/1. Manchester: Urmston.

Energy consumption: efficiency and conservation

Anton J.M. Schoot Uiterkamp

IVEM, Center for Energy and Environmental Studies, University of Groningen, Nijenborgh 4, 9747 AG Groningen, The Netherlands

Introduction

Being alive means consuming energy. An average human being uses the energy equivalent to that of a 150 W ($150 \, \mathrm{J \, s^{-1}}$) lightbulb that has to be kept on continuously. In other words, people need *ca.* 5 GJ (G (giga) = 10^9) of energy a year to sustain their basic metabolic needs. This equals the energy content of $150 \, \mathrm{m^3}$ of natural gas. The 1990 world population of 5.3 billion would have required *ca.* 26 EJ (E (exa) = 10^{18}). The actual world energy use in 1990 was *ca.* 365 EJ, so on average every person used approx. 14 times more energy than the 150 W required for basic bodily maintenance. This 'extra' energy flow represented economic activities that provided valuable human services ranging from space heating and cooling, to cooking and storing food, boiling water, lighting, industrial processes and transportation. If the 365 EJ had been distributed equally throughout the world, each person would have used *ca.* 2200 W or 2.2 kW. In reality, US citizens consumed about five times as much per year, Europeans and Japanese two to three times as much per year and citizens in many developing countries less than half that amount per year.

The situation in 1999 was no different from that in 1990. Apart from the very unequal distribution of energy consumption among people in the world, most energy used (over 90%) is still derived from non-renewable sources such as coal, oil, natural gas and nuclear power. These resources are still relatively large and inexpensive, often owing to government subsidies. However, low-cost non-renewable energy supplies are rapidly running out. Moreover, the environmental impacts of energy use from sources such as fossil fuels are high (Houghton *et al.* 1995). The European CO_2 emissions in 1995 were 8.5 tonnes per person. In brief, production and consumption require energy use, but how much is a matter of continuing debate. One thing is certain: the present world energy system is clearly not sustainable.

The planet can provide the present world population with a sustainable energy supply of 1.5 kW per person from renewable resources (Dürr 1994), about one-third to one-quarter of the present energy consumption per person in western European countries. To bring about a transition towards a sustainable and environmentally acceptable energy consumption and supply, changes are needed throughout the system. Model studies indicate a reduced dependence on energy, plus energy conservation and efficiency improvements, and the large-scale changeover to renewable energy resources such as sunlight, wind and biomass (Mulder & Biesiot 1998). In western European countries, energy efficiency was improving by *ca.* 1% per year during the past decade, in line with the possibility of uncoupling economic growth from energy consumption. Before concentrating further on what these changes mean for European energy consumption, some remarks will be made on corresponding changes in energy supply and relevant energy sources.

Non-renewable energy sources

The European energy supply system is still strongly dominated by non-renewable resources. Among Western-style regions, Europe is unusual in its relatively large dependence on nuclear energy. About one-third of the electricity used in European Union (EU) countries in 1990 was generated from nuclear power. Operating nuclear power plants produce essentially direct CO_2-free electricity (although the indirect CO_2 production is substantial), a great advantage in an era concerned about the effect of greenhouse gases. Nevertheless, nuclear power presents a whole range of other problems ranging from siting difficulties and safety and security concerns to plant decommissioning and the handling and storage of nuclear waste. For all these reasons, the stage in many European countries is set for a shift away from nuclear power. Even in France, which generates over 80% of its electricity from nuclear power, some officials have called for less dependence on nuclear power. In the UK, in contrast, a recent report has expressed the importance of keeping the nuclear option open to provide a secure supply of electricity at an acceptable cost (Royal Society and Royal Academy of Engineering 1999).

In the use of fossil fuels, three trends are predominant. The first is toward more efficient energy generation (see also below). For example, present state-of-the-art combined-cycle gas turbines now produce electricity with over 55% efficiency, a substantial improvement from the 35–40% typical of classical steam power plants. Although much has been accomplished, there is still substantial room for improvement. However, the trends towards the co-generation of heat and electricity and more efficient industrial processes such as steel and glass manufacturing are unmistakable. Secondly, energy generation is becoming cleaner, especially as a result of implementing environmental controls such as flue gas treatment and desulphurization technology. Lastly, but not least, there is a clear trend towards 'decarbonization' (Grübler 1998, p. 287), implying a decrease in the specific amount of CO_2 emitted per unit of energy used. For example, a shift from coal to natural gas for power generation means moving from a source of 94 kg of CO_2 per GJ to a source of 56 kg of CO_2 per GJ^{-1}. If we assume that the overall energy use is not increasing simultaneously, such a shift fits very well in 'post-Kyoto' policies aimed at reducing CO_2 emissions.

Renewable energy sources

Continuing research and investment programmes seek to increase the EU-wide share of energy from renewable sources such as solar, wind, hydropower and biomass from 4% in 1991 to 8% in 2005 (EC Committee of the American Chamber of Commerce in Belgium 1994). Sustainable efforts are under way to achieve this goal. For example, Tomen, a Japanese firm, plans to invest US$1.2 billion in the installation of 1000 large wind turbines in Europe over the next five years; wind generation expanded by 25% in 1997. In Denmark, about 3600 wind turbines generated 3% of the country's electricity in 1994, and the figure is projected to reach 10% in 2005. Initiating and maintaining renewable energy supply systems has its own environmental impacts and socio-economic consequences. In general, energy from non-renewable sources is needed to realize the transition towards renewables. After all, solar cells and wind turbines do not arise spontaneously. In 1997, British Petroleum announced plans to invest US$1 billion in solar and other renewable energy resources over the next several years. Royal Dutch Shell announced similar plans with a commitment of $500 million. Unlike the stock-based non-renewables, renewable sources are flow-based. Because the sun is not always shining and the wind is not always blowing, adequate and effective energy storage systems are needed to maintain energy supply during night-time or calm. All of this has spatial consequences. Unlike subsoil-derived non-renewables such as oil and natural gas, renewable energy sources need space at the earth's surface. However, space is a strictly finite resource, especially in populated areas, where energy is needed most. Spatial functions such as bird sanctuaries and wind power generation are not always compatible, implying difficult societal and environmental trade-offs. The EU target of establishing a market share for bio-fuels of 5% of total motor fuel consumption is illustrative (EC Committee of the American Chamber of Commerce in Belgium 1994). Without an appropriate overall life-cycle assessment this policy target is more an initiative to resolve a problem of excess agricultural food crop production than a solution to an energy or environmental problem. Upgrading biomass such as wheat or wood to motor fuels implies efficiency losses that can be avoided when biomass is incinerated directly to generate heat.

Energy consumption

Energy consumption is a misnomer. Energy is neither consumed nor created. What is consumed is the capacity of a particular form of energy to do work. For example, in a gas-fired electric power plant the chemical energy in natural gas is completely converted into thermal energy that in turn is only partly converted into electricity. Any practical energy conversion results in the loss of some of the energy's capacity to do work.

These losses can be large. Only 3% of the primary energy from a coal-fired power plant is converted into light in a regular light bulb (Von Weizsäcker *et al.* 1997). Before looking into possibilities to decrease useful energy losses, some remarks are needed about avoiding losses by avoiding energy consumption altogether. After all, consumers want so-called 'end-use services' such as illumination and comfort; if these can be provided while conserving energy, so much the better. Von Weizsäcker *et al.* (1997, pp. 160–164) present the fascinating case of Pacific Gas and Electric Company, which helped customers to save electricity by selling them compact fluorescent lamps with rebates. A similar example is the 'negawatt plant' planned for Hanover. Providing customer services such as lighting and heating with highly improved efficiency was equivalent to not constructing a new 300 MW power station (Hennicke & Seifried 1996, p. 122).

Energy efficiency

Western European countries have achieved great gains in energy efficiency since the 1970s. The energy efficiency referred to here is the ratio of the output of a conversion process or of a system to its energy input. Countries expanded their national economies while simultaneously improving energy efficiency. The overall result was that the final energy use of these countries remained about the same. However, Schipper & Meyers (1992, pp. 78–79), presenting data for seven European countries in the Organization for Economic Co-operation and Development and for the USA and Japan, have shown that the relative share of different economic sectors has changed. Whereas the energy use of manufacturing declined from 36% of the total to 27% between 1973 and 1988, passenger travel increased from 19% to 22% and freight transport from 19% to 22%. Lastly, but not least, the residential share grew slightly from 20% to 21%. Detailed studies of the Danish (Wier 1998) and Dutch (Wilting *et al.* 1998) economies are illustrative in this regard. In Denmark between 1966 and 1988, energy conservation was implemented throughout the economy with the exception of transportation fuel. In most economic sectors and in all demand categories like households, export and investments, there has been a shift towards a less energy-intensive composition of inputs and commodities. Both effects have considerably reduced emissions but this has been outweighed by economic growth requiring energy for further production. The period studied showed large fluctuations in energy prices, resulting in a falling demand for commodities from energy-intensive sectors (Wier 1998).

Similarly in the Netherlands, during the period 1969–98, the energy intensity fell in 40 out of 56 economic sectors, with 31 sectors showing a decrease larger than 10%. Again, rising energy prices were strongly correlated with declining energy intensities. Significantly during the period 1969–88, the number of households increased by *ca.* 50%, but the overall increased energy demand of the household sector was *ca.* 30%. The indirect energy demand of households (due to food, clothing, communication, recreation and medical care, for example) increased more strongly than the direct energy demand (due to electricity, heating and motor fuel). The energy intensities of the various production sectors producing foods and services for the household sector decreased less than the corresponding growth in the overall volume of household consumption. In other words, the energy efficiency improvements only partly compensated for the volume growth of the sector. This seems to be a common finding: technological improvements are offset by volume effects resulting from behavioural, social or demographic factors. National governmental and collective EU actions traditionally tended to focus on issues such as stimulating energy-efficient cars, refrigerators and light bulbs, and on subsidizing home insulation and co-generation. Energy-related research and development has mostly reflected this orientation. It is now obvious that technological improvements will not be sufficient to bring about the transition referred to above.

Research agenda

In general, much more attention should be given to interdisciplinary studies of the systems characteristics of the energy supply and demand network and to the (often unforeseen) consequences of actions aimed at reducing energy consumption. This gives rise to a research agenda with a range of topics and questions. For examples, the geographical setting of energy efficient homes might constitute urban sprawl and a corresponding increase in energy-intensive commuter traffic. Energy efficiency improvements might result in so-called rebound effects, i.e. the money saved being spent on energy-intensive activities such as airline travel. Can such phenomena be foreseen and resolved; if so, how? The EU-wide policy towards liberalization of the national power markets to enhance competition by 2005 is another case in point.

As indicated, increasing energy prices have, in recent years, often resulted in energy efficiency improvements due to intensive research, development and manufacturing efforts. Is it possible that large-scale energy consumers in the near future will be more inclined to shop for the lowest prices between competing energy suppliers than to aim for the most energy-efficient technologies? Since electric power networks were built, central power generation has been the preferred option. What are the consequences for electric network management of strongly increased decentralized electric power generation characteristic of photovoltaic devices, wind turbine parks and co-generation plants? In addition, a substantial move towards energy from renewable sources requires a range of easily accessible, environmentally acceptable and cost-effective energy storage facilities. Relatively little R&D is directed towards achieving such a goal. Lastly, the energy consumption in the household sector is more difficult to control than in other sectors of the economy. Studies show that most policies directly aimed at reducing the energy demand of households were either not successful or were only marginally so, with the exception of home insulation programmes. In contrast, policies not directly aimed at reducing energy consumption in households often resulted indirectly in increasing energy consumption, e.g. emancipation policies gave rise to large transportation demands in double-income households (Ligteringen 1998). Much more attention should therefore be given to structures, measures and policy incentives aimed at cost-effectively, feasibly and acceptably reducing household energy consumption without evoking corresponding increases in energy consumption in other economic sectors.

Concluding remarks

There is no lack of models aimed at studying the consequences of various sets of consumption in terms of energy supply and demand. Practical experience from past decades in Europe shows the still incomplete understanding of the main characteristics of the dynamic energy field. The field is influenced by rapidly changing energy prices, unforeseen developments in world population and in world energy demand, technical breakthroughs, efficiency improvements, new policy instruments and geopolitical developments. Lastly, but not least, adverse environmental consequences either in isolation or in combination might serve as powerful warning signals that the future of the overall energy system is not necessarily reflective of its past. Dedicated and non-diminishing attention to all aspects of energy at all levels of society remains necessary for many more decades to bring about a transition towards a truly sustainable energy supply and demand system in Europe as elsewhere.

References

Dürr, H.P. 1994 Sustainable, equitable economics. The personal energy budget. In *The world at the crossroads. Towards a sustainable, equitable and liveable world* (eds P.B. Smith, S.E. Okoye, J. de Wilde & P. Deshingkar), pp 21–38. London: Earthscan.

EC Committee of the American Chamber of Commerce in Belgium 1994 *Brussels: EU Environmental Guide*, p. 80. Brussels: European Commission.

Grübler, A. 1998 *Technology and global change*. Cambridge University Press.

Hennicke, P. & Seifried, D. 1996 *Das Einsparkraftwerk*. Basel: Birkhäuser.

Houghton, J.J., Meiro Filho, L.G., Callender, B.A., Harris, N., Kattenberg, A. & Maskell, K. 1995 *Climate change 1995—the science of climate change*. Cambridge University Press.

Ligteringen, J.J. 1998 The effects of public policies on household metabolism. In *Green households? Domestic consumers, environment and sustainability* (eds K.J. Noorman & T. Schoot Uiterkamp), pp. 212–235. London: Earthscan.

Mulder, H.A.J. & Biesiot, W. 1998 *Transition to a sustainable society; a backcasting approach to modelling energy and ecology*. Cheltenham: Edward Elgar.

Schipper, L. & Meyers, S. 1992 *Energy efficiency and human activity*. Cambridge University Press.

Royal Society and Royal Academy of Engineering 1999 *Nuclear energy: the future climate*. London: The Royal Society and The Royal Academy of Engineering.

von Weizsäcker, E., Lovins, A.B. & Lovins, L.H. 1997 *Factor four—doubling wealth: halving resource use*. London: Earthscan.

Wier, M. 1998 Sources of changes in emissions from energy: A structural decomposition analysis. *Economic Systems Research* **10** (2), 99–112.

Wilting, H.C., Biesiot, W. & Moll, H.C. 1998 Trends in Dutch energy intensities for the period 1969–1988. *Energy* **23**, 815–822.

Economic theories of sustainable consumption

Jeroen C.J.M. van den Bergh* and Ada Ferrer-i-Carbonell†

*Department of Spatial Economics, Free University, De Boelelaan 1105, 1081 HV Amsterdam, The Netherlands

†SEO, Foundation for Economic Research of the University of Amsterdam, Roetersstraat 11, 1018 WB Amsterdam, The Netherlands

Introduction

In searching for sustainable development the term 'sustainable consumption' has arisen. It reflects the realization that all environmental and resource problems caused by humans are ultimately the result of consumption and lifestyles, the important other determinant being population size. Consumption has a central place in economics, where it is regarded as the result of individual or household decision-making under constraints. Here we intend to survey the potential contribution of economic theories to the understanding of policies enhancing 'sustainable consumption'.

Different perspectives on sustainable consumption are closely associated with those in what we refer to as the growth debate (van den Bergh & de Mooij 1999). Pessimists argue that physical and biological limits will hamper any further increase of material consumption. Optimists are confident that scientific and technical progress will allow us to overcome such limits. A more extreme view—as well as a widely held belief—is that growth in income per person changes human preferences in favour of environmental quality. 'Environmental Kuznets curve' research, which has tested this thesis, has shown that it does not hold in general for all environmental problems. Associated with the growth debate is the discussion about the gross domestic product (GDP) as an indicator of progress or welfare. It has been criticized for assuming implicitly that basic human conditions, such as space, direct access to resources (for example Nature or fresh water) and serenity, can be replaced by economic goods such as large apartments, fast cars and expensive holidays. Using the GDP as the single progress indicator implies that the replacement of 'nature' by 'economy' is taken for granted and evaluated as 'progress'. However, this has been questioned in many theoretical and empirical studies (see, for example, Argyle 1999; Daly & Cobb 1989; Easterlin 1974; Jackson & Marks 1999). These seem to support the thesis that the trends in the level and composition of consumption in rich countries, including those in Europe, are unsustainable and do not necessarily contribute to human progress.

Three main questions arise in the context of sustainable consumption. Firstly, what is the relationship between consumption, lifestyles and environmental sustainability? Secondly, what theoretical economic perspectives on consumer behaviour are useful? Thirdly, what kind of economic policies are suggested by the theories to realize sustainable consumption? These questions will be discussed below.

117

Sustainability and consumption

Before going into theory it will be useful to consider the precise interpretation of sustainability in relation to consumption. This section will be kept very short because related issues are discussed in more detail elsewhere in this volume.

'Sustainable consumption' is a term that follows the popularity of combining a particular word with 'sustainable', sometimes leading to an oxymoron. Examples are sustainable agriculture, sustainable city, sustainable growth, sustainable population, sustainable tourism and sustainable transport. Consumption of goods and services requires the direct and indirect use of materials, energy and use of space. 'Sustainable consumption' can, like 'sustainable transport' or 'sustainable city', be assessed only in a system-wide context, i.e. taking into account production, trade, transport, population, resource extraction and waste management. Of course, if 'sustainable' is interpreted as merely 'less polluting' or 'less resource wasting' the (un)sustainability of consumption can be assessed much more easily.

To analyse the causes and consequences of consumption, one needs to develop a system of relevant relationships between determinants of consumption and environmental pressure. Figure 1 shows an example of such a system. Consumption is regarded as dependent on the lifestyle, which has three types of determinant: objective and personal individual (or household) characteristics, the social context or environment, and technological characteristics of the available products. Note that the lists of items mentioned under each general determinant category in the figure are incomplete and merely illustrative.

Each lifestyle can be generally associated with a certain mix of goods for consumption. The classification of these is somewhat arbitrary, and might be adapted for the purpose of environmental impact assessment. This could lead to a distinction on the basis of, for example, durability, 'greenness', energy-intensity, and new versus second-hand products. A detailed distinction used in a study by Jackson & Marks (1999) covers the following components of consumption: food, housing, fuel use, health care, clothing, maintenance, household appliances, communication, catering, books and newspapers, tobacco and alcohol, furniture, recreation and entertainment, travel and other. The environmental pressure can be assessed for each of these. A study of changes in consumption between 1954 and 1994 in the UK shows that the expenditures on 'household appliances' and 'recreation and entertainment' have increased almost fourfold, 'travel' threefold, and clothing twofold; the average increase was *ca.* 100%.

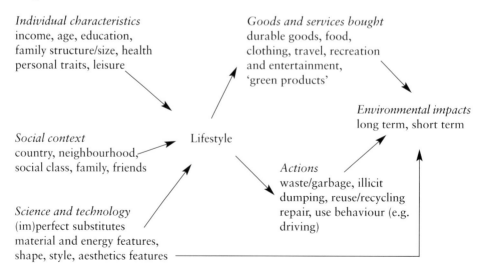

Figure 1. A framework for the study of sustainable consumption.

Next, the scheme in Figure 1 shows an arrow from consumption categories to the environment. The environmental impact of consumption has been investigated in various studies. Energy requirements of durable goods have been studied in the Dutch 'HOMES' project (Noorman & Schoot Uiterkamp 1998). Some studies have analysed environmental impacts of technology and lifestyles by using 'structural economics', based on input–output analysis. To understand sustainable consumption, information about the buying behaviour or possession of goods might be insufficient. As shown in Figure 1, consumption also has a negative effect on the environment through 'actions' other than 'buying behaviour'. These include 'use behaviour' and 'waste behaviour'. The first of these denotes the intensity and manner of use of products, for instance, the style of driving a car. This has an effect on, among others, the energy consumption and lifespan of a product. The second activity covers repair, production of garbage (e.g. packaging material), illicit burning, dumping, reuse and recycling. The total environmental impact of consumption is thus regarded as being determined by the combination of buying, use and waste behaviour, in combination with the expenditures on the various goods and services, and the technological characteristics of the products. The latter comprises both production and waste features. The environmental–technological characteristics of the product can be regarded either as exogenous from the perspective of consumption analysis, or as another determinant of buying, use and waste behaviour (e.g. through cost effects). The second approach, although complicating predictions and frustrating environmental strategies such as 'Factor 4', is probably more realistic.

A theoretical framework for sustainable consumption

In studying consumer behaviour and seeking a complete perspective on the limits and opportunities for sustainable consumption, at least five levels of behaviour need to be considered.

1. **Preferences:** important here are changes in life styles, owing to fashion, income change, availability of new products (i.e. technological change), relative preferences (social environment), influence by other cultures, and influences of mass media. Today, preferences are very much shaped by commercial television, radio and magazines, as well as by the social interaction with individuals that all buy and consume new goods at a high rate. Some have referred to this as the 'affluenza virus'.
2. **Motivations:** different theories of consumer behaviour have been discussed (see Hodgson 1988; van den Bergh *et al*. 2000). The traditional economic model is based on maximizing utility. Other theories include 'satisficing', imitation, habitual or routine behaviour, social or group behaviour, citizen/consumer dichotomy, needs satisfaction and various approaches to behaviour under uncertainty (see van den Bergh *et al*. 2000). Ackerman (1997) argues that recycling does not follow from maximization of utility but from some type of pure altruism.
3. **Constraints:** standard economics focuses on income or budget constraints as a determinant of consumer behaviour. Other constraints include the cultural/social or institutional: working hours, shopping hours, social norms, family contacts, policies, standards and laws (see Røpke 1999). In addition, time budgets can exist for each type of activity (e.g. travel, holidays, cleaning and shopping).
4. **Decisions based on given preferences, goals and constraints:** standard economics can trace the impact of changing prices and income on buying behaviour. On the basis of these insights, consumer-oriented policies or producer-oriented policies (the polluter pays) can be designed. Environmental tax policies change not only prices but also incomes, which

will subsequently affect behaviour. The alternative theories mentioned under level 2 do not always give clearcut results and cannot always be applied or quantified; for these reasons they have been less popular.

5. **Types of decisions relevant for environment impact assessment:** these include buying (or investment, including saving and borrowing money), use, reuse, recycling, repair, illegal dumping and waste treatment. Such a disaggregate approach to consumer decisions has not received so much attention in the economic literature. The various decisions or activities by a consumer are interdependent and should ideally be analysed in a single coherent framework. Again, alternative behavioural models can be applied, notably habitual behaviour and imitation for other than 'main' activities.

All five levels are part of 'consumer behaviour'. Each level can be associated with certain policy implications. For instance, traditional economics largely ignores changes on the first level (Deaton & Muellbauer 1980), whereas psychology and marketing (managerial economics) are particularly interested in these changes.

The dominant neoclassical tradition in economics has assumed the behaviour of individuals to be reducible to the maximization of utility. It regards choices as being easily predictable on the basis of price and income information because individuals are assumed to have invariant preferences, i.e. they show consistent behaviour in different situations and periods (for more details, see van den Bergh *et al.* 2000). The implication is that policy makers can modify consumers' demand in any desired direction by influencing prices or income (level 4 changes). This explains the optimistic attitude towards price-based instruments in environmental economics. Deleting the behavioural assumptions of standard economics means that less importance will be given to such price-based instruments. This is related to the fact that the notion of economic efficiency loses significance if other than utility-maximizing theories are adopted.

On level 1 the notion of 'consumer sovereignty' is important, which has been taken as a starting point in standard economics. It is needed to formulate the utility-maximizing model. Norton *et al.* (1998) distinguish between four degrees of consumer sovereignty: (i) unchanging preferences, (ii) given preferences (disciplinary boundaries), (iii) critique on and policy aimed at preferences inconsistent with democratic principles, and (iv) democratically decided policies aimed at changing preferences. The last is consistent with an approach that allows for 'endogenously changing preferences' as the focal point of environmental policy (level 1). Norton *et al.* (1998) argue that fear of a 'totalitarian government' from following preference-changing policies is unnecessary for several reasons: preferences are already unconsciously manipulated by all sorts of other policies, they are influenced purposefully 'behind the scenes' by all sorts of stakeholders, and commercial companies have long since influenced preferences via the media, purely out of profit motivation. Perhaps most importantly, preference-influencing environmental policies can be based on democratic decisions. The main question is then how preferences change. Economists know little about this. This indicates the need for multidisciplinary research, involving behavioural physiologists, psychologists, sociologists and economists.

On level 2 various theories are available. A few examples can clarify the usefulness of adopting a pluralistic perspective. It is possible to assume that there is a very strict limit to what can be substituted in consumption: people have many basic needs, such as food, shelter, company, respect and freedom. These cannot be traded off against luxurious material consumption. This relates to the economic and psychological concept of lexicographic preferences, which denotes that individuals will first satisfy a 'lower' need (satisfying hunger) before becoming interested in 'higher' needs (recreation). Moreover, people have limited desires and needs, i.e. saturation occurs at certain levels of consumption. According to this view, growth of material consumption, notably in urban and polluted environments, is regarded as no more than imperfect compensation for a loss of basic need satisfaction such as social relations, serenity, space and direct access to Nature. The theory of lexicographic preferences was introduced by Menger. It suggests that the growth of income and material consumption can never act as a substitute for lost environmental, social and other non-market services. Material wealth is most important for the quality of life when basic needs are not yet covered, but loses importance beyond that. Basic needs such as shelter or food are material by definition, while higher needs such as self-esteem or belonging depend mainly on the quality of social relationships.

From the perspective of 'satisficing' bounded rationality and routine-like behavioural models, responses to environmental regulation will not be as evident as in maximizing behaviour. Transaction costs are present everywhere, and imply that 'satisficing' (a combination of 'satisfying' and 'optimising') might be more adequate than optimizing behaviour, because the latter would involve an infinite regression of searching and checking whether all the relevant information has been acquired and used. Both habitual behaviour and 'satisficing' can explain the 'energy gap', i.e. the unreaped economic benefits associated with potential conservation of energy. Economic psychology treats this issue in the context of consumer behaviour models that take account of issues such as visibility, demonstration value, environmental concern, relational knowledge (information), habits and socio-demographic determinants.

Girardian economics focuses on problems of addressing pervasive uncertainty, based on human desires being unstable, humans being ignorant, and events being unpredictable. Market signals (prices and interest rates) provide uncertain clues for decision-making, although prices can be regarded as an indication of quality in highly uncertain markets. Desire and behaviour become mimetic, examples of which are panic selling, spiralling inflation, and speculation. Another implication of uncertainty is the desire for wealth, as an explicit goal and a means of reaching self-sufficiency. Wealth allows people to avoid having to imitate others and to be safe in the face of surprises. This goal of wealth leads to envy (see van den Bergh *et al.* 1998).

The standard economic theory has been criticized extensively for insufficiently addressing the social context of individual behaviour (see van den Bergh *et al.* 1998). One suggestion is that consumers get satisfaction not only from goods themselves but also from the social context, which has been referred to as 'non-functional demand' and 'positional goods'. Such effects imply that environmental policy might have counterintuitive effects on the consumption of certain status goods.

One step further is to assume that welfare is relative, i.e. individual welfare can never be assessed independently from the welfare of other individuals in the relevant social environment—tribe, village, region, country and (because of 'globalization') the entire world. For example, poverty is both an absolute and a relative concept: the 'needs' concept refers to its absolute dimension; the relative dimension is related to the fact that people are likely to be unhappy as a result of not being able to afford goods that most other individuals in their relevant social environment consume.

Some policy implications

The mainstream economic view on policy for sustainability is that all external costs of decisions by producers and consumers are charged to those decisions. More precisely, optimal ('first-best') policy should aim at realizing the optimal price in the (hypothetical) social optimum defined as the situation in which all externalities are accounted for. To arrange environmental sustainability, the external costs should cover not only present externalities but also all future externalities. Because it is impossible to obtain all the necessary information for calculating these externalities (by a planner or market) the ideal policy will resemble a 'fata Morgana'. Tradable permits, although regarded in standard economics as a 'second-best' instrument, are perhaps more suitable in the context of sustainability goals. Many scientists feel comfortable with physical and biological limits associated with environmental sustainability. Economics shows that these can subsequently be linked to marginal prices, based on markets in which permits to pollute or to use resources are traded to the amount of the respective system-wide limit.

Lexicographic preferences can be related to the notion of strong sustainability, in which complementarity, uniqueness and non-substitutability of life support functions, climate regulation, and Nature in general are emphasized. Consequently, policies that try to make trade-offs in an environmental context based on individual preferences might find that individuals are unwilling to make such trade-offs (Stern 1997). This provides support for tradable permits as an instrument for sustainability.

The notion of 'relative welfare' introduces additional uncertainty about traditional environmental policy suggestions. For instance, efficiency will then become dependent on equity. This means that any environmental policy aimed only at efficiency can still not neglect impacts on income or welfare distribution.

A practical and now popular approach to environmental policy is the strategy of 'Factor 4'. It represents a technological perspective on reducing environmental pressure by striving for technological alternatives to existing products and processes that are more material and energy-efficient. Economists have argued that a distinction should be made between direct and indirect effects, or gross and net gains. The term 'rebound effects' is often mentioned in this context, referring to both behavioural and macroeconomic (economy-wide) effects. For instance, more energy-efficient combustion engine cars will reduce the fuel costs of driving, as a result of which people will ultimately drive greater distances (behavioural response). Moreover, the macroeconomic effect is that because of a lower total demand for fuel its price falls, causing a further decrease in the cost of driving, enforcing the behavioural response. (For more discussion of 'Factor 4' see Myers (this volume) and Jordan & O'Riordan (this volume).)

For many people, sustainable consumption has a strongly ethical or normative connotation, denoting that we should completely change our lifestyles and preferences. To achieve this, specific types of policy might be implemented, ranging from education and other 'moral suasion instruments' to very restrictive measures such as a ban on certain types of commercial advertisement. One specific view is that the 'Western lifestyle' should be redefined and modified so as to reduce material consumption and give more importance to social relations and spare time. The latter would not only reduce human impacts on the environment but possibly also improve human satisfaction. For this purpose, utopian, planning or blueprinting views are proposed that focus on simpler lifestyles or incorporate elements of countryside life, compact or garden cities, and technologically advanced means of transport. These typically differ from economic policy views that are based on markets, freedom of individual decision-making and prices as incentives. The problems for analysts created by utopian approaches is twofold. First, they represent such drastic changes relative to the current socio-economic–environmental system that it is unclear how and whether the desired system can be realized. Secondly, for the same reason it is virtually impossible to say anything sensible about the economic implications. Evolutionary models of change rather than our present static type of analysis are needed to understand historical, path-dependent development, lock-in of present technologies and spatial constellations, and the adaptive change to more desirable social systems.

Prospects

Various theoretical economic models of consumer behaviour need to be adapted to an environmental context, taking into account social context, endogenous preferences and actions such as buying goods, use of them, repair, reuse, and waste treatment. Standard economic theory focuses mainly on consumption as a determinant of utility and not as part of a biological (eating, shelter), learnt (fashion, imitation), social (belonging, relative welfare) or cultural (shopping as leisure) activity. Alternative theories of individual behaviour offer interesting views on the motivations of behaviour: 'satisficing', habitual behaviour, avoiding risk, lexicographic preferences, changing preferences, household decision making, and social context of consumption. It seems too ambitious to strive for a general theory. Instead, we plead for a pluralistic approach that recognizes the value of different theories. Each can serve to illustrate particular characteristics of consumer behaviour in reality. Different theories emphasize specific policy measures as being most useful to realize sustainable consumption. For instance: standard economic theory focuses on correct relative prices of less and more pollutive goods and services; sustainability seems to point at tradable permits as a more attractive instrument; relative preference theories focus on stopping the 'rat race of consumerism' via education and public information; and endogenous preference theories imply instruments such as moral suasion and restricting commercial advertisement. It is a challenge to combine these various theoretical insights to arrive at an effective policy package for sustainable consumption.

References

Ackerman, F. 1997 *Why do we recycle? Markets, values, and public policy.* Washington, DC: Island Press.

Argyle, M. 1999 Causes and correlates of happiness. In *Well-being: the foundations of hedonic psychology* (eds D. Kahneman, E. Diener & N. Schwarz). New York: Russell Sage.

Daly, H.E. and Cobb, W. 1989 *For the common good: redirecting the economy toward community, the environment and a sustainable future.* Boston: Beacon Press.

Deaton, A. & Muellbauer, J. 1980 *Economics and consumer behaviour.* Cambridge University Press.

Easterlin, R.A. 1974 Does economic growth improve the human lot? Some empirical evidence. In *Nations and households in economic growth. Essays in honor of Moses Abramowitz* (eds P.A. David & M.W. Reder), pp. 89–125. New York: Academic Press.

Hodgson, G.M. 1988 *Economics and institutions.* Cambridge: Polity Press.

Jackson, T. & Marks, N. 1999 Consumption, sustainable welfare, and human needs—with reference to UK expenditures patterns between 1954 and 1994. *Ecological Economics* **28**, 421–441.

Noorman, K.J. & Schoot Uiterkamp, A.J.M. (eds) 1998 *Green households? Domestic consumers, environment and sustainability.* London: Earthscan.

Norton, B., Costanza, R. & Bishop, R.C. 1998 The evolution of preferences. Why 'sovereign' preferences may not lead to sustainable policies and what to do about it. *Ecological Economics* **24**, 193–211.

Røpke, I. 1999 The dynamics of willingness to consume. *Ecological Economics* **28**, 399–420.

Stern, D. 1997 Limits to substitution and irreversibility in production and consumption: a neoclassical interpretation of ecological economics. *Ecological Economics* **22**, 197–215.

Van den Bergh, J.C.J.M. & de Mooij, R.A. 1999 An assessment of the growth debate. In *Handbook of environmental and resource economics* (ed. J.C.J.M. van den Bergh), pp. 643–655. Cheltenham: Edward Elgar.

Van den Bergh, J.C.J.M., Ferrer-i-Carbonell, A. & Munda, G. 2000 Alternative models of individual behaviour and implications for environmental policy. *Ecological Economics* **32** (1): 43–61.

Sustainable consumption: economic practice

Karl-Göran Mäler

*Beijer International Institute of Ecological Economics, Royal Swedish Academy of Sciences,
PO Box 50005, S10405 Stockholm, Sweden*

Introduction

What is sustainable development and what should we mean by sustainable consumption?

There are many (some would say too many) definitions of sustainable development. The most widespread and the most useful one is the following from *Our common future* (World Commission on Environment and Development 1987, p. 43): 'Sustainable development is development that meets the needs of the present without compromising the ability of future generations to meet their own needs.'

This statement has at least two implications:

- resource use must be such that we leave for future generations assets that give them the possibility of enjoying a level of well-being not lower than we are enjoying today;
- resources must not be depleted 'unnecessarily', that is, the cost of resource depletion must be felt by the resource user so that this person will take into account the effects of the depletion on other members of the current generation as well as on members of future generations.

Consumption is necessarily connected with resource use. This implies that the consumer is using resources in his activities as a consumer. However, the consumer is seldom feeling the total cost of this resource use, mainly because of property rights failures that make resources underpriced in markets. The consumer, in planning offspring, will also contribute to future resource use without having to take the cost of this use into account.

The result of these factors is a level and composition of consumption that is distorted and leads to excessive resource use, now and in the future. This means that the consumption pattern is probably not sustainable and is surely not socially desirable. Sustainable consumption can therefore be defined as a consumption pattern that reflects the scarcities of all resources that are used in producing consumption goods.

Incentive structures

The ultimate causes of these distortions are the lack of property rights to resources which prevents their scarcity values to be revealed on markets. The first step in reducing the distortions is therefore to try to improve the property rights structure. However, that will be impossible in many cases, because the resources are public goods that cannot be divided into individually owned pieces. Examples are many: climate, local air pollution, and coastal and marine ecological systems. In these cases, either user rights or taxes might be tried. User rights mean the right of an individual or an organization to use a resource up to a certain limit. If these rights can be made transferable, there will be a market price on these rights that will capture the cost of using the resource within the total limit on the resource use that society has decided. The resource cost is made visible! Taxation of resource use would have a similar effect. In both cases, incentives will be created to reduce the use of the resource and increase the cost of using it. This will also increase the prices of those goods that use the resource more intensively relative to other goods, with obvious effects on the demand for the goods. Thus, measures to 'fix the prices' on natural resources (including the use of the waste assimilative capacity of the environment) will have effects on the final composition and level of demand for goods for consumption (for further discussions see Mäler (1974) and Dasgupta & Mäler (1995)).

However, there are many situations in which it is impossible to implement these incentive structures. One example is when we cannot monitor the resource use in any precise way; another is when the jurisdiction of the resources belongs to a non-cooperating nation. In these cases it might be desirable to implement commodity taxes such that the tax rate reflects the scarcity of the resources embodied in the commodity. Such taxes can be administered (but at some cost because our systems for indirect taxation are based on more uniform taxes) and they will change the composition of consumption away from resource-intensive commodities towards more environmentally friendly commodities. However, they will also have some impacts on the choice of technologies (that is, how resource-intensive a commodity shall be).

Intertemporal aspects

The correct scarcity value of a resource is the present value of the future marginal values of the resource. This present value depends on two factors: the future marginal values and the discount rate. The present market interest rates are often determined for very short timespans. In contrast, natural resources might have good uses for extremely long periods. That means that the discount rate must be determined on different grounds from simply using the market rate. There are now some tools for doing this (Barrett *et al.* 1996). Basically, these tools try to make models for the future and from those deduce the implications for the interest rate.

A growing population in an economy with an unsustainable consumption pattern will obviously aggravate the problems caused by the unsustainable pattern. If the pattern cannot be corrected completely, it might therefore be desirable to create incentives to reduce population growth, so as to reduce the future distortions.

International aspects

Almost all consumption goods are traded internationally. This means that if one country tries to reduce its resource use by, say, taxing it, its export of commodities using this resource will be less competitive and will therefore fall. This reduction in production in one country might be completely or more offset by increased production in other countries (if other countries are producing the same commodities but with higher resource intensity, the resource use will increase). Furthermore, the cost to the country that tries to conserve its resource might be quite high. It is therefore essential that these attempts are made with an international, cooperative approach. Furthermore, this might also be necessary because of commitments through international organizations such as the World Trade Organisation.

This problem also arises when a country tries to implement a set of commodity taxes with the objective of changing the consumption pattern. This could be regarded as measures for strengthening the country's own competitive position, and other countries might retaliate. Once again, international cooperation is necessary. There is now a growing literature on the economics of using environmental policies for strategic trade (Rauscher 1997).

Finally, actions to change the consumption pattern in the North might affect the South negatively. If a poor country wishes to develop its economy through development of a particular resource, actions in the North (for example by taxing all commodities, imported or domestically produced from this resource), the poor country will effectively be blocked from economic development. This might happen, for example, if the rich countries agree on imposing a carbon tax. In these cases, it seems reasonable to create a flexible system that will give the South a fair chance to exploit its resources or compensate the South for taking away these chances.

References

Barrett, S., Dasgupta, P. & Mäler, K.-G. 1996 *Intergenerational equity, social discount rates and global warming*. Discussion paper 91. Stockholm: Beijer International Institute of Ecological Economics.

Dasgupta, P. & Mäler, K.-G. 1995 Poverty, institutions, and the environmental-resource base. In *Handbook of development economics* (ed. J. Behrman & T.N. Srinivasan), vol. 3. Amsterdam: North-Holland.

Mäler, K.-G. 1974 *Environmental economics: a theoretical inquiry*. Baltimore: Johns Hopkins University Press.

Rauscher, M. 1997 *International trade, factor movements and the environment*. Oxford University Press.

World Commission on Environment and Development 1987 *Our common future*. Oxford University Press.

The role of trade in sustainable consumption

Paul Ekins

School of Politics, International Relations and the Environment, Keele University, Staffs ST5 5BG, UK and Forum for the Future, 227a City Road, London EC1V 1JT, UK

Consumption and the environment

In economic terms, production is an activity that uses various forms of capital, in particular human and manufactured capital, to add value to other inputs to production, to create goods and services for which there is a consumer demand. Consumption then involves the generation of utility for the consumer through the using up, or subtraction, of the value added in production.

Again, in conventional economic terms, the sustainability of production and consumption depends on whether the capital stock that creates the goods and services is maintained. This requires that out of each period's production sufficient be invested, rather than consumed, to make up the depreciation incurred by the capital stock in the production process. In these terms, consumption will be sustainable if it is not too high for adequate resources to be available for investment.

Recently, however, concerns have arisen that production and consumption might not be sustainable because of the impact that they are having on the natural environment. There are worries about the environmental, rather than the economic, sustainability of economic activity. The two kinds of sustainability are linked because the environment itself, through its provision of resources, absorption of wastes and maintenance of life-support processes, makes an important input into economic activity. It is feared that if the environment becomes too depleted or degraded it will be unable to provide these inputs, leading to reduced production (and therefore reduced consumption) or a direct loss of welfare (which can be viewed as equivalent to reduced consumption) or both. The sustainability of consumption in this case depends on a sustainable use of the environment. In some environmental economic literature, this environmental sustainability is linked to the conventional condition for economic sustainability by viewing the environment as 'natural capital'. The sustainability of production and consumption then requires that the stock of natural capital is maintained, either separately from, or as part of, the total capital stock, depending on whether the different kinds of capital are viewed as interchangeable (substitutable) with each other or not. It is well understood that market processes by themselves will not necessarily lead to sustainable use of the environment (maintenance of natural capital), because many of the environmental effects of economic activity remain external to, or are incompletely accounted for in, the relevant market transactions. For environmental sustainability to be achieved in such a situation, one or more of three changes must come about:

1. Producers must voluntarily embrace the sustainable use of environmental resources. In a competitive market it will be difficult for producers to do this individually if they thereby incur significant costs.
2. Consumers must voluntarily take account in their consumer decisions of the environmental impacts of consumption (including those involved in the production, use and disposal of the relevant good or service). This requires not only that their preferences for environmental sustainability are sufficiently strong to make them willing to pay any additional costs involved, but also that they have the required information about the environmental impacts of the production, use and disposal of various goods and services to enable them to give effect to these preferences.
3. Governments must give incentives to or compel, through either financial instruments or legislation, either producers or consumers, or both, to use environmental resources sustainably. This is increasingly becoming the purpose of environmental policy or, more broadly, attempts to move societies towards 'sustainable development'.

Consumption and trade

Increasingly, consumers are consuming goods and services that have been produced in other countries. Between 1950 and 1990, world trade increased elevenfold to *ca.* US\$3.5 trillion (1990 values) (French 1993, p. 7), over twice as fast as world product. Between 1990 and 1995 world product increased by 17%, but trade increased by nearly 30% (International Monetary Fund 1998, pp. 154–155 and 166–167). In Europe, economic output increased by an average of 2.5% per year from 1980 to 1990, whereas its exports grew at 3.0% per year over the same period. Thereafter the increase in European trade accelerated markedly. During 1990–1994, a period of slow growth of only 0.9% per annum in Europe, its exports increased at over 4% per annum (United Nations 1997, Special Table F, p. S118).

This increase in world trade has not come about by accident. Rather, it has been systematically promoted through the progressive liberalization of world trade by the General Agreement on Tariffs and Trade (GATT), entered into by industrial countries after World War II but now subscribed to by over 100 nations, accounting for the great majority of the world's output.

Trade liberalization has considerable implications for the three means of moving towards environmental sustainability noted in the previous section:

1. It makes markets more competitive. This reduces the discretion of individual producers voluntarily to incur costs of environmental protection, even where they might wish to do so.
2. It lengthens supply chains. This makes it more difficult for consumers to obtain the information about the environmental impacts of the production of the goods and services that they are consuming, even when they wish to take this into account in their consumer decisions. There are some examples of consumers seeking to factor social and environmental considerations into their purchase of products from abroad. For instance, the International Institute for Environment and Development (IIED 1997) ten case studies of market success and low environmental impact in manufacturing, tourism, agricultural commodities and forest products. However, such initiatives still account for only a tiny proportion of world trade, and the information requirements for consumers to exercise effective choice in this way are heavy. Moreover, even the information labels that would seem to be essential for such choice can be, and have been, regarded as discriminatory barriers to trade in contravention of the GATT Articles (see below). For example, when in 1992 the Austrian Parliament passed a regulation requiring all tropical

timber to be labelled, a threat of trade sanctions and of a GATT challenge by Malaysia resulted in the regulations being withdrawn (Cairncross 1995, pp. 230–231).

3. Governments are constrained by GATT concerning the restrictions, or charges, that they can place on imported goods. These constraints interact with environmental policy-making in a number of ways, and might make it more difficult for governments to legislate for sustainable production and consumption.

These effects are among those that have led to a heated debate on the relationship between trade and the environment. The debate has so far been inconclusive because of the wide range of possible positive and negative effects of trade and its liberalization on the environment, and the difficulty of acquiring definitive empirical evidence to ascertain the overall net effects of their interaction.

The possible positive effects of trade liberalization can be listed as follows.

- Trade liberalization promotes economic growth; indeed, this is its principal purpose. As societies become richer, there is more political interest in protecting the environment and more resources to do so.
- Trade liberalization promotes the efficient allocation or resources, allowing the production of a given economic product with the least possible use of resources.
- Trade liberalization promotes the international transfer of environmentally preferable technologies.
- Trade liberalization promotes the convergence of environmental standards for products and processes towards the higher levels of rich countries, and increases the markets for environmentally preferable products.
- Trade liberalization promotes international cooperation in other areas, notably environmental protection.

The negative effects are as follows.

- Trade liberalization amplifies environmental externalities through its promotion of economic growth.
- Trade often involves long-distance transport, which is one of the principal sources of environmental externalities.
- Because of pressures of competitiveness, trade liberalization will result at best in political drag on environmental policy-making by governments, and at worst in an environmental 'race to the bottom' through competitive deregulation.
- Trade rules arising from trade liberalization impede national governments in their attempts at environmental protection, either because of possible trade effects (e.g. through mandatory reuse of containers) or because of perceived discrimination (e.g. eco-labelling).
- Trade rules can exclude the use of trade measures in multilateral environmental agreements.
- The production of some highly traded goods (e.g. cotton, cigarettes, certain foods) is more environmentally destructive than the production for domestic consumption that it replaces.
- Opportunities to use land for trade result in subsistence farmers' being displaced onto environmentally marginal land, where they cause environmental damage.

The importance of the rules of world trade in the above list is obvious. Consideration of trade and sustainable consumption therefore cannot get far without looking in detail at the GATT rules and their effect on environmental policy-making.

GATT and the environment

Of the three international economic institutions proposed after the World War II, two—the International Bank for Reconstruction and Development (World Bank) and the International Monetary Fund—were formally established. The third, the International Trade Organisation (ITO), was only realized as a General Agreement on Tariffs and Trade. GATT came into force in 1948. By 1991, 103 states were formal Contracting Parties to GATT, including the 24 industrialized countries that comprise the OECD (Organization for Economic Co-operation and Development) and account for 75% of world trade, and another 29 states were applying GATT on a *de facto* basis.

GATT rules, expressed in Articles, provide the essential framework conditions for most world trade and seek to embody for GATT's Contracting Parties 'reciprocal and mutually advantageous arrangements directed to the substantial reduction of tariffs and other barriers to trade and to the elimination of discriminatory treatment in international commerce' (GATT 1986, p. 1).

GATT Articles are amended, or their scope is enlarged, by periodic 'Rounds' of negotiations, of which the Uruguay Round, begun in 1986, was the eighth. The principal objectives of the Uruguay Round were to bring agriculture, textiles and services within the scope of GATT for the first time, and to formulate rules for trade-related investment and trade-related intellectual property. In 1991 the GATT Secretariat inserted a proposal in the Draft Final Act of the Uruguay Round to establish a World Trade Organisation (WTO), reminiscent of the original ITO proposal, to subsume GATT in future. The proposal was adopted as part of the Uruguay Round, and the WTO was established when the Uruguay Agreement came into force in January 1995.

The GATT Articles are founded on the principle of non-discrimination in trade with regard to:

1. Trading partners—any country that is a GATT signatory must accord all other GATT signatories the same trading conditions as it accords to its 'most favoured nation';
2. National treatment—like products, these must be treated in the same way irrespective of their country of origin.

Article XX permits limited exceptions to these 'most favoured nation' and 'like product' principles, including exceptions related to the conservation of natural resources, but so far there has never been an environmental dispute under GATT in which an exception on these grounds has been upheld.

In 1992 the GATT Secretariat spelt out what environmental protection is compatible with current trade rules (GATT 1992, p. 23):

> GATT rules … place essentially no constraints on a country's right to protect its own environment against damage from either domestic production or the consumption of domestically produced or imported products. Generally speaking, a country can do anything to imports or exports that it does to its own products, and it can do anything it considers necessary to its production processes.

After the Uruguay Round agreement in 1994, this formulation somewhat overstates a country's discretion on policy towards the environment and human health, for the new agreement requires policies in these areas that have trade effects to be based on 'scientific evidence' if they are not to be open to challenge from another country that feels them to be too stringent. Given substantial scientific uncertainty in many issues related to the environment, there is likely to be a wide margin of interpretation of what constitutes 'scientific evidence' in these cases. Neither is it clear that the WTO possesses the scientific expertise to make judgements in this area.

In a related area, that of food safety, considerable influence on scientific issues, and therefore power to adjudicate on food safety, has been granted by the WTO to the Codex Alimentarius Commission. Although Codex is jointly financed by the UN Food and Agriculture Organization (FAO) and World Health Organization (WHO), concern has been expressed that it is unduly influenced by transnational corporations (Evans & Walsh 1994, p. 23; Lang & Hines 1993, pp. 100–103; National Consumer Council 1998, pp. 96–97). It might therefore be more attuned to business and trade priorities than to safeguarding human and animal health, and either discourage or disallow regulations stricter than Codex-agreed international standards, which some countries and interest groups perceive as being too lax.

Even leaving to one side the problem of what constitutes 'scientific evidence', the GATT pronouncement quoted above about what a country can do to protect the environment throws into sharp relief what it cannot do under GATT rules.

- It may not use trade policy to protect its environment from foreign production. It could not impose trade sanctions, for example, on a neighbouring country that persistently exported air or water pollution, no matter how damaging its effects.
- It may not use trade policy to protect the environment outside its own jurisdiction, whether a global commons or the territory of another country. GATT rules do not currently envisage the possibility of trade measures being applied in support of, for example, the provisions of the Montreal Protocol (discussed below), the Framework Convention on Climate Change or the Law of the Sea.
- It may not impose on imports charges or other restrictions related to their process and production methods (PPMs), even when it is imposing identical treatment on its own production (i.e. its policy is non-discriminatory). This obviously acts as a major discouragement to apply strict environmental policy measures to production processes where it is perceived that such measures might have a negative effect on the competitiveness of domestic business.
- Some environmental regulations can be deemed inadmissible as technical (or non-tariff) barriers to trade. GATT rules require such regulations to be the least GATT-inconsistent that are available. Esty (1994, p. 48) comments: 'This sets an almost impossibly high hurdle for environmental policy, because a policy approach that intrudes less on trade is almost always conceivable and therefore in some sense "available"'.

From an environmental point of view these GATT-prohibitions impose considerable constraints on environmental policy. There follow some examples that illustrate how such provisions under GATT have either brought trade liberalization, trade rules and environmental policy into conflict, or might do so.

The US/Mexico tuna–dolphin dispute

In 1991 the USA banned Mexican-caught tuna from the US market on the grounds that the Mexican fishermen killed an excessive number of dolphins when fishing for tuna in the Eastern Tropical Pacific Ocean. Further to a challenge from Mexico, a GATT Panel ruled that the US ban was GATT-illegal because it related to PPMs and resulted in discrimination against 'like products' (tuna) and because the USA was seeking to apply its laws outside its jurisdiction.

In fact, the way in which the USA applied the regulation that led to the ban was clearly discriminatory against Mexico (as the GATT Panel also found) in that the permissible dolphin–kill ratio (number of dolphins killed per net dropped) was defined retrospectively based on what the US fishermen had achieved. There was therefore no way in which Mexican fishermen could know in advance how many dolphins they could kill without triggering the US ban. This aspect of the case raises the clearest suspicions that the US action was at least partly motivated by commercial and not environmental considerations. Its trade measure could easily have either specified a maximum dolphin kill ratio, equally applicable to Mexican and US fishermen; or banned tuna caught with certain kinds of net (whether by US or Mexican fishermen) from the US market and insisted on inspection and certification arrangements to validate this. Had it done so, the measure might still have been deemed GATT-incompatible (on grounds of extrajurisdictionality and the irrelevance of PPMs), but at least it would be clear that the USA was seeking purely environmental, and not commercial, gain.

Another GATT ruling went against the USA when it was challenged in 1992 for seeking to ban tuna imports from third countries that had first imported the tuna from Mexico. This time the Panel called into question the ability of any country to use the GATT exemptions clause, Article XX, for any kind of unilateral trade restriction (for further discussion of the tuna–dolphin case see Esty (1994), pp. 30–31 and 268–269, and Brack (1995), pp. 501–502).

In the event, neither of the judgements was adopted by the GATT Council, but they infuriated environmentalists and did much to provide the political impetus for the environment-trade campaign, which resulted in the subsequent incorporation by the North American Free Trade Agreement (NAFTA) of an environmental side agreement, and which turned trade and the environment into a major international issue.

The trade provisions in the Montreal Protocol

A number of international environmental agreements contain trade provisions (listed in Andersson *et al.* 1995, pp. 117–119), of which the most important are probably the Convention on International Trade in Endangered Species (CITES, in 1973), the Montreal Protocol on Substances that Deplete the Ozone Layer (1987), and the Basel Convention on the Control of Transboundary Movements of Hazardous Wastes (1989), of which the second is briefly discussed here.

The Montreal Protocol contains trade provisions relating to parties to the Protocol, insofar as imports of ozone-depleting substances (ODS) are subject to the control schedules, and relating to non-parties with regard to trade in ODS themselves, in products containing them and, potentially, in products manufactured with them. These provisions are complex and have been examined in detail elsewhere (Brack 1996). Here it need only be noted that the reports of the GATT tuna–dolphin Panels (Brack 1996, p. 72) appeared to cast considerable doubts over the GATT-compatibility of the Montreal Protocol. Its control measures lead to quantitative restrictions on trade; its trade provisions directed against non-parties can be applied against WTO members who are not Protocol signatories, and envisage trade restrictions on the basis of process and production methods (PPMs); and both sets of measures could be regarded as extrajurisdictional.

The Montreal Protocol has gained the accession of the great majority of countries (150 by 1995), and has fixed stringent controls on the production of ODS that have greatly reduced the quantities that would otherwise be in circulation. Many observers of, and participants in, the Protocol process believe that the trade provisions made an important contribution to these achievements. Clearly the uncertainty that still surrounds them does not help with the negotiation of future international environmental agreements that might benefit from such provisions, and it reinforces the perception of environmental insensitivity with which the WTO is sometimes regarded.

The US/Venezuela gasoline reformulation dispute

New rules made by the US Environmental Protection Agency (EPA) under the 1990 Clean Air Act Amendment required that from 1995 all gasoline sold in the USA had to be of a cleanliness equal to or greater than that sold in 1990. Domestic refiners were allowed to qualify for an individual baseline standard derived from documentation of their gasoline formulations in and after 1990. Importers, however, had to meet an imposed standard based on the average for the US industry.

Venezuela, later joined by Brazil, appealed to the WTO in 1995, alleging discrimination. The USA sought to defend itself with the Article XX exceptions relating to health and the conservation of resources (in this case, clean air). The final WTO judgement accepted that air was a 'depletable resource' under the terms of Article XX, and accepted the relevance of the health exception in this case, but found in favour of Venezuela and Brazil because the USA could have achieved its environmental goals in a less discriminatory way, namely by setting a single standard for domestic producers and importers (ITLR 1996).

Because, unlike in the tuna–dolphin case, the regulation was applied to a product, there was no challenge to the USA's setting the standard. However, as with tuna–dolphin, the unnecessarily discriminatory way in which the regulation was formulated leads to suspicion that commercial as well as environmental protection was an objective of the measure.

The Danish bottles case

In the early 1980s Denmark instituted a mandatory deposit-refund system for drink containers and, to facilitate their reuse, stipulated that container designs would need to be approved by the Government. Foreign producers objected that the regulation was discriminatory against them, because the system effectively ruled out containers other than glass, which were more expensive to transport, and prevented product differentiation through innovative packaging design. On challenge, the European Court ruled in 1988 that the deposit-refund was a legitimate means for Denmark's pursuit of its environmental objectives, which were in turn justified by the European Community's commitment to environmental protection. However, it also ruled that the stipulation on container designs acted as a disproportionate restraint on trade compared with the environmental benefit that it yielded, and so it was disallowed (Esty & Geradin 1997, pp. 297–299). Had the challenge been brought to GATT, it might well have been that the deposit-refund system would have been disallowed as well, because GATT had no general commitment to environmental protection and the system might well have been found disproportionately trade-restrictive.

The Finnish carbon tax

Finland was the first country to introduce a carbon tax, in 1990, which has evolved into a wide-ranging carbon-energy tax. Economic theory suggests, and Finland's own studies confirmed, that a carbon tax would be the most effective instrument to curb carbon emissions, which was the aim of the tax. Thus coal, the most carbon-intensive fossil fuel, bore a carbon-energy tax that was 78% carbon-related (Teir 1996, p. 246).

About 10% of Finland's electricity is imported and the marginal generating fuel is coal, so that the Finnish carbon-energy tax had potentially serious implications for the competitiveness of domestic coal-fired generation, to address which Finland levied a tax on imported electricity at a rate that was the average of the Finnish carbon-energy tax on electricity overall, but still only about half that on coal-generated electricity. However, even this tax on imported electricity is considered to run counter to the Treaty of Rome because Finnish electricity, as such, is untaxed. Neither European nor WTO trade regulations permit a tax on imports to balance input taxes on domestic production.

The result was that, at the end of 1995, the Finnish Government decided to remove its carbon tax and replace it with an overall tax on electricity, which would comply with the trade rules. However, the electricity tax will be substantially less effective at reducing carbon emissions because it will do nothing to encourage switching to low-carbon fuels in electricity generation, which, in other countries, is one of the principal ways in which CO_2 reductions have been achieved.

The European Commission's carbon-energy tax

In 1992, just before the Rio Summit, the European Commission introduced its proposal for a carbon-energy tax as one of its proposed measures to reduce carbon emissions so as to mitigate climate change. The proposal exempted the six most energy-intensive industrial sectors, was made conditional on a similar tax being introduced in North America and Japan, and recommended both that governments should introduce it on a revenue-neutral basis and that tax rebates should be given against investments in energy efficiency. Nevertheless, the tax was vehemently opposed by the business community. 'Activities undertaken independently by companies, national trade associations, European trade association and industry confederations such as UNICE (Union of Industrial and Employers' Confederations of Europe) added up to a major anti-tax campaign' (Ikwue & Skea 1996, p. 100).

The principal argument employed by business in its campaign was that the tax would have a negative effect on corporate and national competitiveness. In fact the exemptions and other proposals would have rendered the economic impacts minimal in practically all sectors. According to Ikwue & Skea (1996, pp. 101–102), 'The key issue remains one of trust. Industry does not trust governments to introduce such a measure without turning it into a revenue-raising device at some point in the future. The tax is seen as "the thin end of a wedge"'. Reduction in competitiveness was the most important threat that such a wedge represented. Yet the need for international competitiveness is enhanced by trade liberalization. Notwithstanding the growing realization of the advantages of environmental taxation in environmental policy-making, this will be very difficult to introduce in a systematic and broad-based way where it is perceived to threaten competitiveness.

The shrimp–turtle dispute

In 1987 the USA, pursuant to its Endangered Species Act, issued regulations requiring all shrimp-trawl vessels to take steps to reduce their incidental take of sea turtles (an endangered species) while harvesting shrimp. By 1990 the regulations required the use of turtle-excluder devices (TEDs) at all times.

In 1989, Section 609 was enacted, which required the US Secretary of State to open negotiations with all countries engaged in commercial shrimp harvesting, to arrive at an international agreement, or agreements, to protect sea turtles. Section 609 also provided for a ban on shrimp imports to come into force in 1991, where the shrimp were harvested in such a way as might have affected sea turtles, unless the fishing operations of the harvesting nation had been certified by the US Government as posing no greater a danger to sea turtles than the operations of the US fishing fleet.

The 1991 guidelines applied only to countries in the Caribbean/western Atlantic region, but in 1996 the application of the regulations was extended to all countries. In addition, the US Court of International Trade ruled that the ban had to be applied to all shrimp imports from uncertified nations, even where the shrimp involved had been harvested using TEDs that complied with US domestic regulations. India, Malaysia, Pakistan and Thailand complained that the import ban violated the WTO Articles, and a dispute Panel was established in February 1997.

The Panel reported in May 1998 (WTO 1998a). It found that the US import ban was in violation of Article XI, which prohibits the imposition of import restrictions on trade between Members, and that the ban was not covered by the 'exceptions' article, Article XX. In fact, the Panel ruling seemed to question whether the Article XX exceptions could ever be applied by a Member, on the grounds that, if other Members applied such exceptions, this 'would threaten the security and predictability of the multilateral trading system'.

The USA appealed against this ruling, and the WTO Appellate Body gave its judgement on the Appeal in October 1998 (WTO 1998b). It reversed the Panel's decision on Article XX, finding that the US measure itself was legitimate under the terms of the Article. However, it also found that the way in which the USA had applied the measure involved 'unjustifiable and arbitrary discrimination', and therefore was not consistent with Article XX. This conclusion rested largely on the Appellate Body's view that 'it is not acceptable, in international trade relations, for one WTO Member to use an economic embargo to require other Members to adopt essentially the same comprehensive regulatory program, to achieve a certain policy goal, as that in force within that Member's territory, without taking into consideration different conditions which may occur in the territories of those other Members' (WTO 1998b, para. 164).

The Appellate Body's conclusion also derived from the facts that:

- the USA had banned shrimp imports from uncertified countries even when they were caught under conditions which complied with US regulations;
- the USA had failed to consult adequately before imposing its worldwide ban on shrimp imports;
- the USA had not made adequate efforts to resolve the problem of the sea turtles through bilateral or multilateral negotiations, before imposing its unilateral ban.

The USA has to comply with the Appellate Body's ruling, thereby bringing its trade measure on sea turtles into compliance with the WTO Agreement, by the end of 1999.

Removing the trade obstacles to environmental policy

It should not be impossible to design conditions under which countries can pursue sustainable development to their desired extent within an orderly multilateral trading system, but without constraint from it on their environmental policy-making. Such conditions might require the following.

- The policies must be specific with regard to the seriousness of the environmental damage that they are seeking to address and where this damage is being or will be felt.
- Esty (1994, p. 283) adopts a three-point categorization of environmental harms: serious (rapid, major, certain irreversible harms), moderate (less rapid, major and certain or reversible harms), and limited (least certain, slower, reversible or narrower harms). Provided that the environmental damage physically affects the country concerned, or the global commons, and unless the damage is both limited and reversible, both the policy necessary to address it, and trade measures to enforce it, should be deemed legitimate. No distinction with regard to these environmental policies should be drawn between those directed at products and those directed at PPMs.
- Eco-labels to facilitate the provision of information to consumers concerning the life-cycle

environmental impacts of goods and services, with regard to the products themselves and their PPMs, should be considered fully compatible with WTO articles.

- The environmental policies and measures derived from them must be legislatively non-discriminatory between foreign and domestic producers or products. With regard to eco-labels, for example, it is possible that, in the Austrian case mentioned above, the proposed eco-label would have been less controversial if it had been applied to temperate as well as tropical timber. The policies should also be introduced only after due notice (e.g. twelve months) has been given, during which international agreement with potentially affected parties should be sought that would make the measures unnecessary.

If the GATT rules had been consistent with these suggestions, clearly the arguments in the case studies discussed earlier would have been very different, but it is interesting to note that the trade measures involved would still not necessarily have been immune from challenge. For example, in the tuna–dolphin case it was noted above that the GATT Panel ruled that the US ban was GATT-illegal because it related to PPMs and not products and because the USA was seeking to apply its laws outside its jurisdiction.

Under the proposals above, neither of these reasons would have invalidated the US ban. However, Mexico would have had several other possible grounds of challenge.

1. The killing of the dolphins could be considered a 'limited and reversible' environmental harm. Dolphins are not classed as an endangered species and it could be argued that the taking of 30 000 dolphins per year out of a population numbered in millions (Esty 1994, p. 188) is sustainable.
2. The application of the US ban could be deemed discriminatory (and the GATT Panel ruled it so) in that, as noted above, the permissible dolphin–kill ratio (number of dolphins killed per net dropped) was defined retrospectively based on what US fishermen had achieved.
3. The USA proceeded to its ban without giving formal notice to Mexico of its intent to do so; it did not try less drastic measures first. Interestingly, Esty (1994, p. 251) observed: 'The US tuna ban … had very little practical effect on Mexican exports to the United States because the demand for Mexican tuna had collapsed as a result of commercial and consumer pressures, intensified by the US tuna-packers voluntary dolphin-safe labelling scheme. The market for tuna lacking the dolphin-safe label almost completely dried up.'

Under the terms of the proposals set out above, the GATT Panel could well have come to the same conclusion about the US ban, but for different reasons. Similar considerations apply to the gasoline reformulation dispute. It would have been quite possible to design the detailed regulation differently such that it attained the same level of environmental protection but did not discriminate against non-US refineries. Only in the Danish bottles case, given that the regulation addressed a Danish physical environmental problem, would the above suggestions have made the regulation unequivocally GATT-compatible.

The shrimp–turtle dispute is different from the tuna–dolphin case, in that sea turtles are undoubtedly an endangered species. Moreover, countries could gain exemption from the import ban by requiring the same TED technology as the USA, without waiting for turtle-catch limits to be announced. Undoubtedly US procedures for consultation and for trying to achieve multilateral agreement on sea turtle protection could have been improved before the imposition of the ban, but the judgement against the USA in this case was principally based on a WTO presumption against PPM-based trade measures, which does not seem compatible with the WTO's commitment to sustainable development where global environmental issues are concerned. Had the Panel's decision on Article XX been allowed to stand, Article XX would have effectively become a dead letter. The Appellate Body's slightly less restrictive interpretation still renders it formidably difficult for the purpose of Article XX—to permit exceptions to the other WTO Articles for specific reasons—to be given practical effect.

Threats to competitiveness

One approach to seeking to allay fears of effects on competitiveness from environmental policies involves the progressive harmonization of environmental standards or policies. There is undoubtedly some scope for this, and Esty & Geradin (1997, pp. 283–294) explore in some detail various approaches to potential harmonization that still take some account of differences between countries. However, such a process is bound to be slow in a global community in which these differences—economic, social and environmental—are so profound.

Another approach is to seek to minimize effects on competitiveness by announcing the policies well in advance and introducing them gradually enough to give industry time to adjust to them. This is standard good practice for policy-making in general but might not allow environmental problems to be addressed quickly enough or might give too much time for organized interests that are profiting from unsustainability to mobilize against or water down policy proposals.

Finally, there is the possibility of allowing border tax adjustments (countervailing duties (CVDs) on imports, or export rebates for exports) to offset the effects of environmental policies on competitiveness in both domestic and foreign markets. This response is the one generally favoured by environmental organizations (see, for example, Arden-Clarke 1993), when it is often coupled to a suggestion to return the revenues raised by CVDs to developing countries to help to finance environmental improvements. The practical problems associated with this response are formidable: the cost-internalization approach to calculating the level of CVDs is often infeasible because of the complexity of the environmental effects concerned; the proposal raises the keenest fears among developing countries of an environmental smokescreen for commercial protectionism; its implementation could involve a substantial bureaucracy; and the means of disbursement to developing countries of funds collected would be difficult to design, establish and control.

However, even a recent report from the WTO on trade and environment seems to accept that the political drag from concerns about competitiveness is proving a serious impediment to environmental policy-making, citing the following as arguments that deserve to be taken seriously:

- 'that the legal provisions of the WTO circumscribe the tools available for environmental policy-making' and
- that international trade 'undermines the regulatory power of individual nations'—'the perceived costs of acting alone in terms of lost investments and jobs often take the steam out of new regulatory initiatives' (Nordström & Vaughan 1999, p. 59).

In these circumstances, a commitment to sustainable development might require the introduction of a way of mitigating effects from environmental policy on competitiveness. It should surely be possible to devise a means of achieving this such that world trading rules are not undermined. For example, the ability to levy CVDs on imported products (or give export rebates to exported products), where these have been given a competitive advantage (or disadvantage) by domestic environmental legislation, could be subject to provisos that restrict their scope to physical, transboundary environmental problems, which limit the

CVDs or export rebates that may be applied and that render them open to challenge. The purpose of permitting CVDs to be introduced on these terms would be to remove the influence of arguments about competitiveness from environmental policy-making, by permitting companies that can show genuine disadvantage from it to be protected from its effects for a limited period while they adjust to the new reality.

Surprisingly, the actual textual changes to the WTO articles that would be required to implement the foregoing proposals on international environmental agreements, environmental regulations and CVDs are very few. What is overwhelmingly required is a change of interpretation of the current WTO articles, rather than their wholesale redrafting. This applies principally to Article XX, which seems to give significant scope for the protection of the environment and the health of living things but, as noted in the examples above, various restrictive interpretations have significantly narrowed this scope. In addition, the suggestion about permitting a levying of CVDs to give limited protection against competitive disadvantage arising from environmental protection would require a new sub-clause in Clause 8 of Article III (on national treatment of like products) to the effect that the provisions of Article III would not apply to the kinds of limited protection described above.

Even though it is predominantly reinterpretation of the WTO rules rather than their redrafting that is required, it will not be easy for the WTO to address these issues in a way that both wins international consensus and satisfies those who are concerned with them. There will be a temptation to try to proceed with business-as-usual and avoid the full negotiations on the issues that are increasingly seen to be necessary. The complete failure of the work to date of the WTO's Committee on Trade and Environment to make any substantial progress on the environmental issues that it has considered has already done much to confirm in environmentalist eyes the essential insensitivity of the WTO to the environment. This in turn contributes to the growth of protectionist forces, which are inclined to reject the objective of a broadly open international trading regime altogether.

Conclusion

The current trend towards trade liberalization and global markets makes it more difficult for producers, consumers and government to make more sustainable use of the environment or to move towards sustainable consumption. What is required, to remove this conflict between freer trade and environmental protection, is primarily a reinterpretation of the relevant GATT Articles to permit governments greater scope in discriminating between products, and process and production methods, so as to reduce environmental impacts.

A new round of trade negotiations is now in prospect at which the trade–environment issue is likely to be prominent. Almost certainly the changes in interpretation of the GATT Articles that are required to deal with it effectively will need to be accompanied by financial provisions to ease the transition to sustainability for poorer countries, which will otherwise continue to be suspicious that the greening of the WTO is protectionism in disguise. Richer countries have the choice between making this investment in sustainability now and waiting until the pressures of unsustainability in an ecologically interdependent world erode the possibilities of global cooperation and security and, perhaps, of civilized life itself.

References

Andersson, T., Folke, C. & Nyström, S. 1995 *Trading with the environment*. London: Earthscan.

Arden-Clark, C 1993 *Environment, competitiveness and countervailing measures (paper presented to OECD* workshop on Environmental Policies and Industrial Competitiveness, January 28 and 29 1993, Paris, mimeo). Gland, Switzerland: WWF International.

Brack, D. 1995 Balancing trade and the environment. *International Affairs* **71** (3), 497–514

Brack, D. 1996 *International trade and the Montreal Protocol*. London: Royal Institute of International Affairs/Earthscan.

Cairncross, F. 1995 *Green, Inc.: a guide to business and the environment*. London: Earthscan.

Esty, D. 1994 *Greening the GATT: trade, the environment and the future*. Washington, DC: Institute for International Economics.

Esty, D. & Geradin, D. 1997 Market access, competitiveness and harmonisation: environmental protection in regional trade agreements. *The Harvard Environmental Law Review* **21** (2), 265–336.

Evans, P. & Walsh, J. 1994 *The EIU guide to the new GATT*. London: Economist Intelligence Unit (EIU).

French, H. 1993 Costly trade-offs: reconciling trade and the environment. Washington, DC: Worldwatch Institute.

GATT (General Agreement on Tariffs and Trade) 1986 *The text of the General Agreement on Tariffs and Trade*. Geneva: GATT.

GATT (General Agreement on Tariffs and Trade) 1992 Trade and the environment. In *International Trade 1990–91*, pp. 19–48. Geneva: GATT.

Ikwue, A. & Skea, J. 1996 The energy sector response to European combustion emission regulations. In *Environmental policy in Europe: industry, competition and the policy process* (ed. F. Lévêque), pp. 75–111. Cheltenham: Edward Elgar.

IIED (International Institute for Environment and Development) 1997 *Unlocking trade opportunities: Case studies of export success from developing countries*, a report for the UN Department of Policy Co-ordination and Sustainable Development (UNDPCSD), IIED, London/UNDPCSD, New York.

International Monetary Fund 1998 *International Financial Statistics Yearbook 1998*. Washington, DC: International Monetary Fund.

ITLR (International Trade Law Reports) 1996 United States standards for reformulated and conventional gasoline: commentary, Report of the Panel (17th January 1996), Report of the Appellate Body (29th April 1996). *International Trade Law Reports*, vol.1. London: Cameronmay.

Lang, T. & Hines, C. 1993 *The new protectionism: protecting the future against free trade*. London: Earthscan.

National Consumer Council 1998 *Farm policies and our food: the need for change*. London: National Consumer Council.

Nordström, H. & Vaughan, S. 1999 *Trade and environment*. (Special Studies no. 4.) Geneva: World Trade Organisation.

Teir, G. 1996 The evolution of CO_2/energy taxes in Finland. In *Environmental taxes and charges: National experiences and plans*, papers from the Dublin Workshop, February 7–8 1996, European Foundation for the Improvement of Living and Working Conditions, Dublin, and Office for Official Publications of the European Community, Luxembourg.

United Nations 1997 *1996 International Trade Statistics Yearbook*. New York: United Nations.

WTO (World Trade Organisation) 1998a *United States—import prohibition of certain shrimp and shrimp products, Report of the Panel, WT/DS58/R, May 15 1998*. Geneva: WTO.

WTO (World Trade Organisation) 1998b *United States—import prohibition of certain shrimp and shrimp products, Report of the Appellate Body, WT/DS58/AB/R, October 12 1998*. Geneva: WTO.

Sustainable consumption in Europe: legal aspects

James Cameron and Jürgen Lefevere

Foundation for International Environmental Law and Development (FIELD),
46–47 Russell Square, London WC1B 4JP, UK

Introduction

Sustainable consumption as a concept is now linked with a set of policies designed to influence behaviour across European society: eco-labelling, eco-efficiency, life-cycle analysis, green procurement policies by both government and the private sector through the management of the supply chain, access to information provisions, eco-auditing and integrated pollution control. These policies are all, in some degree, backed by law. Voluntary eco-labelling schemes create no legal obligations in themselves but are governed by advertising standards and the law regarding misleading claims. They can also engage trade rules both at the European and international (WTO) level. Life-cycle analysis is not itself a mandated discipline on industry but might become part of the packaging legislation promulgated at the European level and extended to the 'take-back' regimes for certain products such as batteries and electronic goods.

European cooperation to promote sustainable consumption

Legal instruments in relation to sustainable consumption in Europe are not only found within the separate states in Europe, but since the mid-1970s they have also been found increasingly at the European level, drafted and adopted within European regional organizations. Three of these organizations have been particularly active in the field of environmental policy in general, including the Council of Europe and the United Nations Economic Commission for Europe (UN-ECE) and most importantly the European Community (EC), which since 1993, after the famous Treaty of Maastricht, is mostly referred to as the European Union (EU). None of these organizations have set up a specific body of law and policy in the area of sustainable consumption. Instead, they are increasingly making the goal of sustainable consumption part of their wider environmental policy. This shows a shift in their use of legal instruments from legislation regulating the direct impact of human behaviour on the environment to instruments aimed at promoting sustainable consumption patterns. To get a good indication of European legislation in the area of sustainable consumption it is therefore necessary to give an overview of aspects of the environmental legislation that are relevant for the issue of sustainable consumption.

The actions of none of the European organizations match the comprehensiveness of the legislative efforts undertaken within the framework of the EU. A large part of the environmental policy and especially legislation of the now 15 Member States of the EU is determined by the developments in EU environmental law. Estimates show that between 50% and 85% of all national environmental legislation in EU states is based directly on EU environmental legislation. The influence of EU environmental law has also spilled across its borders. States surrounding the EU are increasingly taking EU environmental law as an example, often for trade-related reasons or in preparation of a prospective membership of the EU. When discussing European developments in legislation concerning sustainable consumption, the EU environmental policy is therefore the best starting point.

EU environmental policy and sustainable consumption

In 1972 the European Union (then still the Community), decided to reinterpret its goal of economic development in a qualitative way, putting the quality of life on a level equal to economic growth. This reinterpretation allowed the development of a comprehensive environmental policy, the main elements of which are laid down in five-yearly environmental action programmes. On the basis of these policy programmes, hundreds of legal instruments have been adopted, covering a wide range of environment-related areas.

Like the conventions adopted under the auspices of the other European regional organizations, much of the EU environmental legislation is focused on the protection of specific parts of the environment from human impacts. Since the beginning of the 1990s we can observe a change in the focus of EU environmental legislation, moving towards a more comprehensive approach and increasingly taking sustainability, including sustainable consumption, as its starting point.

This new approach was introduced in the 5th Environmental Action Programme (5th EAP), entitled 'Towards Sustainability', which was adopted in 1993 and runs until 2000. The 5th EAP no longer focuses solely on environmental problems, but also on human activities that deplete natural resources and damage the environment. In addition it aims at changing society's patterns of behaviour, using a 'partnership' and 'bottom-up' approach, increasing the involvement of industry and European citizens in the development and implementation of environmental legislation. Parallel to the development of the 5th EAP, the Maastricht Treaty, entering into force in 1993, added the concept of 'sustainable growth' to the goals of the EU. The Amsterdam Treaty, which came into force on 1 May 1999, replaced that concept of sustainable growth by that of 'sustainable development'. This has all had an important impact on the development of concrete EU legislative measures that contribute to the goal of sustainable consumption. Although it goes too far to give a full description of all EU measures, a number of important developments need to be mentioned here.

Since the beginning of the 1980s, national eco-labelling schemes have been developed in a number of EU Member States: Finland, Sweden and Norway together introduced the 'Nordic Swan', in Spain the 'AENOR Medio Ambiente' and in Catalonia 'El Distintiu' were created, the Netherlands introduced the 'Milieukeur', Germany the 'Blaue Engel' and Austria the 'Umweltzeichen'. All these national schemes are based on the same principle. If products meet a number of criteria concerning their production, use and after-use, their producers can apply for permission to use the eco-label. The eco-label is printed on the product and its packaging. It allows environmentally conscious consumers to make an informed choice, taking into account the environmental impact of the product that they intend to purchase, including for instance the energy consumption of the particular product or the way in which it was produced. Many of these eco-labelling initiatives have proved to be an important tool in raising awareness of the environmental impact of products and their production methods among both consumers and producers. In Germany, for instance, the Blaue Engel is generally considered to be a success. Covering over 5000 products from almost 1000 producers it has in practice rendered the eco-label criteria the general standard for goods sold in Germany. In reaction to these national eco-labelling initiatives, the EU created in 1992 a Union-wide eco-labelling scheme. The EU eco-labelling regime currently covers over 200 products from 15 product groups, including paints and varnishes, washing machines, tissue paper products and bed-linen and T-shirts, and is still expanding.

In 1993 the EU adopted the Eco-Management and Audit (EMAS) Regulation. This Regulation establishes a voluntary system of eco-auditing for industrial sites. Companies that wish to register one or more of their sites need to comply with a number of requirements, including setting up an internal environmental management system, allowing an independent ecological audit of this system and the publication of the audit results. The EU is currently reviewing the EMAS Regulation and is considering introducing a logo that participating companies can use on their letterheads and other informational material.

In 1996 the EU adopted the Integrated Pollution Prevention and Control Directive. This Directive leaves the earlier 'end of pipe' approach of Community-wide emission standards and instead takes a 'clean technology approach', forcing manufacturers and authorities to consider the emissions of the whole plant. It requires an integrated permit for larger industrial installations, containing limits on emissions to water, air and land, set on the basis of the principle of Best Available Technology (BAT). In addition, the directive requires the quality and emission standards laid down in other EU legislation to be taken into account as a minimum.

Another important initiative is the EU Directive on Packaging Waste, which was adopted in 1994. Packaging waste is responsible for up to 40% of all household refuse. The Directive requires Member States to reduce their packaging waste, to recover between 50% and 65% of the total weight of all packaging waste and to recycle between 25% and 45% of the recovered packaging waste, with a minimum of 15% per material by June 2001. Stricter targets for the period after 2001 are currently being discussed. Part of these discussions will be the use of a life-cycle analysis for reducing packaging waste, and the promotion of reusable packaging methods.

The past few years have also seen a major restructuring of earlier EU environmental legislation in the area of water and air. Until recently, the legislation in this area was very fragmented, often adopted in relation to very specific environmental problems. The new approach is more integrated and aims at limiting the impact of human activity to a sustainable level, comparable to the development of an 'environmental space' for both water and air. The new legislation in the field of air pollution, the Directive on Ambient Air Quality Assessment and Management, was adopted in 1996. The Directive provides for the establishment of new ambient air quality standards and objectives, combined with provisions on the assessment of air quality, and the drafting and implementation of air quality improvement programmes. Most innovative is, however, the proposal for the restructuring of the EU water legislation. The proposal currently under discussion will, if adopted, introduce the concept of integrated river basin management. Until now the water quality legislation has focused on specific water uses, such as drinking water, bathing water and shellfish water, without providing a general framework. In addition, the old legislation focused only on quality issues, not covering the important issue of water quantity. The new proposal requires, for each river basin district, which can cross national frontiers, a 'river basin management plan' to be drawn up. This plan combines the protection of habitats, surface water quality, groundwater quantity, drinking water resources and the protection of bathing water, with the objective of reaching a 'good status' for all waters by the year 2010.

An interesting development is the establishment of various Europe-wide initiatives promoting 'green purchasing' by both government and industry. One of these initiatives is the setting up of the green purchasing network in December 1997. This network aims at promoting green purchasing as an 'essential component' of sustainable development strategies and exploring 'new forms of co-operation' between the public and private sectors to promote sustainable consumption. The network is currently drafting general principles on green purchasing for use by local authorities and companies.

Finally, another initiative that needs to be mentioned is the work currently undertaken by the EU on establishing an Integrated Product Policy (IPP). Rather than focusing on one aspect of the product such as its manufacturing or disposal, IPP is intended to apply to the whole life-cycle of the product with the aim of reducing its environmental impact.

Sustainable consumption in Europe: future challenges

The EU is a unique example of a transboundary approach to environmental problems, more easily setting aside sovereignty issues that so often hinder the development of environmental law on a global scale. The EU's advanced level of environmental legislation is increasingly allowing it to be an important driving force in international environmental negotiations. In addition, the developments within Europe are often seen as examples for either international or regional action in other areas of the world.

However, the EU is still very far from providing the ideal legislative framework based on the goal of sustainable consumption. A large number of important challenges still have to be faced. Of these challenges, two have recently been put high on the political agenda: **implementation** and **integration**.

Developing environmental legislation, actually applying it in practice, and reaching the goals and standards provided for in this legislation are three different stages, all needed for successful implementation. Until recently the EU focused mainly on the development of legislation, without giving much attention to its putting into practice. Implementation problems are now increasingly coming to the surface, often brought to the attention by individuals, who are discovering and learning to use EU environmental legislation. However, environmental legislation is still considered as the EU policy area in which the gap between policy and practice is the widest. The EU is now adopting measures to improve the implementation situation. These measures include improving the knowledge of EU environmental legislation within the Member States, stepping up the Commission's control over its implementation in the Member States, improving the quality of EU environmental legislation, and achieving greater transparency of legislative and enforcement procedures. A central role in the increased implementation effort is also played by the European Network for the Implementation and Enforcement of Environmental Law, the IMPEL network. This network brings together representatives of environmental regulating and enforcement bodies of the Member States, to exchange the experiences in the application and enforcement of EU environmental legislation. The work of IMPEL has recently led the Commission to propose a recommendation providing for minimum criteria for environmental inspections in the Member States. However, significant efforts are required for reaching an acceptable level of implementation.

Integration is another challenge featuring prominently on the EU's agenda. Environmental problems are by their very nature cutting across many different policy areas. Until recently, the integration of environmental concerns into areas of EU policy, such as energy policy, transport policy, agricultural policy, fisheries policy and development policy, was very limited. The EU has now started to tackle the integration issue. The Treaty of Amsterdam put the requirement of integration of environmental policy in other policy areas prominently in the new Article 6 of the European Community Treaty. Anticipating this, the Commission published in 1998 a strategy for integrating Environment into EU Policies. In response to this, the European Council endorsed in its meeting in Cardiff in June 1998 the principle that major policy proposals by the Commission should include an environmental assessment. In addition the European Council in its conclusions 'invited all relevant formations of the Council to establish their own strategies for giving effect to environmental integration and sustainable development'. Initially the transport, energy and agriculture ministers were invited to start the process by producing reports on the integration efforts in their sectors. More recent European Council meetings have expanded this invitation to the other Council formations, including the internal market, industry, development, economic and finance, fisheries and general affairs. Integration was also one of the discussion topics at the European Council meeting in Helsinki in December 1999, which asked the Council to prepare for June 2001 comprehensive integration strategies, including a timetable for further measures and a set of indicators.

An important impetus for the strengthened integration effort has been the adoption under the United Nations Framework Convention on Climate Change (UNFCCC) of the Kyoto Protocol in December 1997. This Protocol will, when ratified, oblige the EU to reduce its emission of greenhouse gases to 8% of 1990 levels between 2008 and 2012. In the area of energy, action is already being undertaken under several programmes such as the ALTENER programme (for the promotion of renewable energy resources), the SAVE programme (Specific Action for Vigorous Energy Efficiency) and the JOULE-THERMIE programmes (non-nuclear energy programmes). However, reaching the Kyoto target will require more substantial efforts, also in other important, and controversial, policy areas such as transport and agriculture, which the EU has yet to prove that it is capable of.

Conclusion

The EU has shown that it is capable of taking important legislative initiatives towards reaching the goal of sustainable consumption in Europe, placed within a wider EU-wide environmental policy. However, as the European Environment Agency in its 1998 report *Europe's environment: the second assessment* has painfully shown, substantial efforts are needed to sharpen these initiatives and their implementation in practice.

Europe needs institutional devices to connect international agreement constantly with domestic and local action, so that the consumer and the negotiator of global accords are linked. It needs procedural devices for integration that systematically engage decision-makers wherever they are in government with environmental concerns. People remain essentially pragmatic when it comes to their needs but will move towards the ideal for their wants. Governments that make law in the public interest and on trust for society must offer leadership towards sustainability. Governments are big consumers in themselves, so they can set an example through procurement policy. They can reward and punish behaviour through fiscal and regulatory instruments and they can create institutions to enable the freest and fullest expression of the political will of civil society.

Further reading

Golub, J. (ed.) 1998 *New instruments for environmental policy in the EU*. London and New York: Routledge.

Sands, P. 1995 *Principles of international environmental law. I. Frameworks, standards and implementation*. Manchester and New York: Manchester University Press.

Appendix A. Statement from the Regional European Meeting on the Transition to Sustainability, at Bled, Slovenia, June 1999

Sustainable consumption—a European viewpoint

1. Consumption is defined here as the human transformation of solid materials, liquids and energy. It is of concern when the transformed materials, liquids and energy become less available for future use or negatively impact biophysical systems in such a way as to threaten human health, welfare and things people value. Unsustainable consumption is a serious impediment to sustainable development.

2. Drivers of consumption are multiple and complex. They should not be attributed to a single factor such as population growth since they involve economic activity, unequal distribution, technology choices, social values and lifestyle, institutions and policies.

3. Scientific and technological advances can address food production efficiency, solar energy capture, new energy sources, creation of new materials and better quality products, and the development of clean technologies. Doing more from less is of paramount importance if we are to shift towards sustainable consumption.

4. Radical attempts to raise awareness about the problem of unsustainable consumption lead to questions about material and non-material values in multicultural societies. Proposals so far include the introduction of 'realistic' resource prices (e.g. traditional market cost plus cost of externalities) having regard to long-term scarcity and environmental impact; adequate laws and regulations for enforcement; redesign of indicators of national productivity and quality of life by the use of environmental economics and a reformulated tax system; removal of market distortions introduced by perverse subsidies that damage the environment; and strengthened mechanisms for international cooperation and decision-making.

5. A special case is Central and Eastern European countries in transition from a planned to a market economy. This change has raised tremendous expectations for rapid economic growth to increase living standards and solve the existing structural problems. Here, too, it is necessary to raise awareness about the sustainability of the projected growth and about the development of sustainable consumption patterns.

6. *Transition to sustainability* is the title of an international symposium to be held in Tokyo, May 2000. Papers from Europe will focus on the question of ways to move towards sustainable consumption—potentially the most challenging issue of the next century. The challenge will demand the combined efforts of scientists, technologists, economists and social scientists. Science and technology alone cannot meet sustainability standards without altered consumption patterns led by changes in human behaviour.

Appendix B. Towards Sustainable Consumption: Statement of The Royal Society of London and the US National Academy of Sciences, June 1997

1. The Councils of the Royal Society of London and the United States National Academy of Sciences see an urgent need for better understanding of human consumption and related behaviours and technologies, so that effective action may be taken to expedite the transition to a sustainable, desirable life for the world's people in the coming century. It has often been assumed that population growth is the dominant problem we face. But what matters is not only the present and future number of people in the world, but also how poor or affluent they are, how much natural resource they utilize, and how much pollution and waste they generate. We must tackle population and consumption together.

2. In developing our thoughts on this matter, we are concerned primarily with the long-term quality of life of all peoples. For the poorer countries of the world, improved quality of life requires increased consumption of at least some essential resources. For this to be possible in the long run, the consumption patterns of the richer countries may have to change; and for global patterns of consumption to be sustainable, they must change. Science and technology are needed to devise and implement effective policies.

Background

3. In 1992 the Officers of the Royal Society and the National Academy of Sciences issued a joint statement *Population Growth, Resource Consumption and a Sustainable World*. It focused on world population and highlighted the consequences of continuing population growth, the urgency of the problem and the contributions that scientific research could make to its mitigation. This statement led, in 1993, to a conference of the world's Science Academies in New Delhi. Fifty-eight Academies agreed a further statement on population, which emphasized that:

    > Resource use, waste production and environmental degradation are accelerated by population growth. They are further exacerbated by consumption habits, certain technological developments and particular patterns of social organization and resource management. ... Scientists, engineers and health professionals should study and provide advice on ... transitions to economies that provide increased human welfare with less consumption of energy and materials.

4. The United Nations has just completed a series of five conferences on major issues of long-term global significance. The conferences concerned environment and development (Rio, 1992), population growth (Cairo, 1993), social factors including poverty (Copenhagen, 1994), women (Beijing, 1995), and the future of cities (Istanbul, 1996). But none of these conferences adequately addressed the issue of resource consumption.

5. An informal network of the Science Academies of the world, the InterAcademy Panel on International Issues (IAP), was formed after the New Delhi meeting to facilitate further collaboration. IAP is now launching a major initiative on the science and technology aspects of moving to a globally sustainable way of life. This will culminate in a conference in the year 2000 and publication of an agreed statement. The conference, and supporting activities developed at regional level throughout the world in preparation for it, should include extensive work on consumption and related issues.

Consumption: defining and understanding the issue

6. Consumption can be defined in the terms of several different disciplines, such as economics, physics, ecology or sociology. The physical concept of transformation of materials and energy provides the basis for a definition of practical value.

    Consumption is the human transformation of materials and energy. Consumption is of concern to the extent that it makes the transformed materials or energy less available for future use, or negatively impacts biophysical systems in such a way as to threaten human health, welfare or other things people value.

7. This definition implies that understanding consumption and making decisions will involve technological and economic choices and processes, such as choosing energy options that involve least direct and indirect cost. It will also require value judgments that are not readily expressed in monetary terms, such as the importance to a society of old-growth forests or other natural areas, or choices of how to meet non-material human needs. Consumption involves producers and distributors as well as 'consumers': for example, the amount of energy and materials transformed in making a car and the quantity of fuel needed to propel it a given distance are as important as the number of cars bought and total miles driven.

Consumption and sustainability

8. We need to understand consumption in the context of sustainability—that is, whether our present actions sacrifice the ability of future generations to meet their needs. The rate of transformation of energy and materials that is sustainable depends on:

    - the rate of natural regeneration of resources;
    - the capacity of the environment to assimilate effluents without substantial negative impact on human health and the biosphere; and
    - the rate at which more abundant alternatives or substitutes can replace energy sources and materials of limited availability.

9. We draw two major conclusions.

    First, in many cases research is needed to assess what consumption rates are sustainable. For example, the rate of regeneration of renewable resources must be understood, alternative resources must be identified, and pollutants and their effects must be analyzed further. We need to know the indicators of sustainability, and whether unambiguous signals can be expected before it is too late to preserve a resource base in economically feasible ways.

    Second, we do now know about many pollutants and their effects. The present rate of consumption and reasonable projections of future rates already indicate that many renewable and non-renewable resources are being drawn down. Also apparent, whatever parameter of consumption is used, is the fact that a relatively small fraction of the world's population consumes a disproportionate amount. The consumption of the most affluent part of the population is of great importance in itself and influences the consumption patterns and aspirations of others worldwide. The poor peoples are rightly seeking to improve their standard of living, and will continue to do so.

Consumption, population growth and technology

10. Some examples illustrate that the phenomenon of consumption concerns more than simple population growth.

    - The population of Bangladesh is increasing by about 2.4 million per year, while that of Britain is increasing by about 100 000 per year. Yet, because carbon dioxide emissions per person in Britain are 50 times higher than in Bangladesh, the 100 000 people in Britain cause more than double the carbon dioxide emissions of the 2.4 million people in Bangladesh.
    - Since 1950, the richest 20% of the world's population has increased its per capita consumption of meat and timber two-fold, its car ownership four-fold and its use of plastics five-fold. The poorest 20% has increased its consumption hardly at all.
    - The impact of increased consumption varies from one commodity to another. Because iron-ore is abundant, and steel can be recycled, their consumption by rich countries need not be at the expense of poor countries. But this may not be the case for commodities that are relatively scarce or cannot be recycled.

11. Moreover, aggregated national data of this sort understate the differences between rich and poor in each country. These divergences are growing in countries at all stages of development.

12. Historically, the pattern has been for consumption of energy and materials **per unit** of GDP (the energy and materials intensity) to rise quickly as a country develops, and then to decline. For example, the energy intensity of industrialized countries has been declining since the mid-1970s. These trends raise important issues.

    - How can such increases in energy and materials efficiency be accelerated to achieve dramatic improvements?
    - Can developing countries skip over the historical maxima of consumption per unit GDP to achieve improved quality of life more quickly and efficiently?
    - Can concepts of industrial ecology and clean production be implemented in developing countries as well as in industrialized countries?

13. Per capita use of petroleum feedstocks in the US is seven times the world average. Gasoline in the United States is cheaper now than at any time in the last sixty years. That price does not reflect even the more immediate indirect costs such as local pollution. And the developing countries are following the example of rapid adoption of the automobile: last year, more new cars were sold in Asia than in Western Europe and North America together. How can technology and investment be mobilized to provide the world with less consumptive and polluting transportation, unless the industrialized countries lead the way? Some useful progress has been made in increased fuel efficiency (miles per gallon) and in reduced emissions, but can these and further improvements be implemented globally?

14. Such examples demonstrate that consumption depends on a range of interacting factors: population, economic activity, technology choices, social values, institutions, policies. The question remains whether, even if consumption per unit GDP decreases, a global GDP adequate for a decent life for the world's rapidly increasing population can be achieved at consumption levels that are sustainable. And it forces us all to consider what constitutes a 'decent life'.

The way forward on consumption: science and society

15. The research and action agenda implied by these considerations is urgent and ambitious. That agenda requires identifying the critical factors and setting priorities among many efforts. These efforts include:

    • vigorous research on sustainable energy sources and on energy efficiency in all its forms, and vigorous promotion of those technologies for energy efficiency that already exist;
    • development and diffusion of environmental technologies;
    • research on ways of defining and determining environmental costs, and on incorporating them into pricing and taxation policies;
    • improvement of energy- and land-efficiency of food production;
    • management, protection and regeneration of natural systems;
    • minimization, recycling of materials and of components, and re-use of waste streams; and
    • development of new and replacement materials.

    There are increasing numbers of successful cases where products made with less transformation of materials and energy and less environmental impact have at the same time made firms more profitable. The same is true of waste streams: for example, Minnesota Mining & Manufacturing mounted a pollution prevention program that has to date eliminated more than half a million tons of pollutants, with savings of $750 million. Such cases must be understood and multiplied.

16. At the same time, societies need to examine their values and consider how goals can be met with the least damaging consumption. Scientists can help to understand the causes and dynamics of consumptive behavior. They can also develop indicators that track environmental impacts and link them to consumption activities, build understanding of how environmental and social systems respond to stress, and analyze the effectiveness of different strategies for making and implementing policy choices in the presence of uncertainty.

17. These are exciting challenges. Social and natural scientists can and must work with private firms and public officials to produce innovations and the incentives to implement them, locally and globally. As scientists but also as citizens of the world, we must strive to see that its riches are used in such a way that our descendants throughout the world can continue to enjoy them. We hereby emphasize our intention to help stimulate these important efforts by the international community of scientists.

Appendix C. Sustainable consumption: useful websites for governmental and non-governmental publications

The views expressed on these websites do not necessarily reflect those of The Royal Society or its associated organizations.

Centre for New American Dream:
   http://www.newdream.org
Clearing-house for Applied Futures:
   http://www.agenda-transfer.de
Consumers International: A Matter of Living on Earth:
   http://www.consumersinternational.org
'Consumption in a Sustainable World' workshop convened from 2–4 June 1998 in Kabelvåg, Norway, sponsored by the Norwegian Ministry of Environment:
   http://www.iisd.ca/sd/norway/sdvol16no1e.html
Demos:
   http://www.demos.co.uk
Development Alternatives:
   http://www.ecouncil.ac.cr/devalt/dagrp.htm
Economics and Sustainable Development: Towards a Systems Framework
   http://www.iisd.ca/vanlennep/
Europe's Environment: The Second Assessment
   http://www.eea.eu.int
European Commission DG XXIV: Consumer Protection and Consumer Health Policy:
   http://europa.eu.int/en/comm/dg24/spc.html
European Green Purchasing Network:
   http://www.epe.be/gp.html
European Society for Ecological Economics: Transitions Towards a Sustainable Europe:
   http://augenblix.wu-wien.ac.at/esee2000/
Eurostat:
   http://www.eurostat.html
Food and Agricultural Organization:
   http://www.FAO.org
Friends of the Earth, Sustainable Societies:
   http://www.xs4all.nl/~foeint/ssp.html
Global Action Plan for the Earth:
   http://www.epe.be/epe/database/members/gap.html
GRIP Centre for Sustainable Production and Consumption (Norwegian Green Management Programme):
   http://www.grip.no
International Council for Local Initiatives:
   http://www.iclei.org
International Energy Agency:
   http://www.iea.org/energy.htm
International Institute for Energy Conservation
   http://www.iiec.org
International Institute for Environment and Development:
   http://www/iied.org/

International Institute for Sustainable Development:
  http://www.iisd.ca/linkages/sd/
IUCN/Economics
  http://www.economics.iucn.org
Material Evidence: Practical Recommendations for National and European Resource Use:
  http://www.foe-Scotland.org.uk/campaign/sure/suresummary.html
New Economics Foundation:
  http://www.neweconomics.org
New Road Map Foundation:
  http://www.newroadmap.org
OECD Project on Environmentally Sustainable Transport:
  http://www.193.51.65.78/env/trans/grphpage/est.htm
OECD Work Programme on Sustainable Consumption and Production:
  http://www.oecd.org
Oxford Commission on Sustainable Consumption
  http://users.oc.ac.uk/~ocees/
Population Action International
  http://www.populationaction.org
Programme for Research and Documentation for a Sustainable Society:
  http://www.prosus.nfr.no
Redefining Progress:
  http://www.rprogress.org
SAFE Alliance:
  http://www.gn.apc.org/safe
Stockholm Environment Institute:
  http://www.sei.se
SustainAbility Limited:
  http://www.sustainability.co.uk
UK Department of Environment, Transport and the Regions:
  http://www.detr.gov.uk
United Nations (ESCAP):
  http://www.unescap.org/stat/statdata
United Nations Division for Sustainable Development and International Institute for Sustainable Development: New and Innovative Policy Instruments for Change in Consumption and Production Patterns:
  http://iisd.ca/susprod/
United Nations Earth Summit updated statistics:
  http://www/un.org/esa/earthsummit
United Nations Environment Programme: Global Environment Outlook 2000:
  http://www/unep.org/unep/eia/geo2000
United Nations Environment Programme Work Group on Sustainable Production:
  http://unep.frw.uva.nl/
United Nations Programme on Measuring Changing Consumption and Production Patterns:
  http://www.un.org/esa/sustdev
United Nations Development Programme: Human Development Report:
  http://www.undp.org/undp/hdro
World Business Council for Sustainable Development: Sustainability through the Market:
  http://www.wbcsd.ch
World Resources Institute:
  http://www.wri.org

Worldwatch Institute
  http://www.worldwatch.org
Wuppertal Institute:
  http://www.wuppertal.org